BACKS

A Common Sense Approach to Back Injury Prevention

BY

LEONARD RING

M.Sc. (Erg.U.K.) F.Erg.Soc.(U.K.) M.C.S.P.(U.K.)

Published 1993 by UNIPRINT, University of Auckland, New Zealand.

ISBN 0-473-01832-2
U.S.A. Copyright Registration No. TXU 546 811

"Society is always being taken by surprise
at some new examples of common sense."

EMMERSON

CONTENTS

Part 1. The Training Objectives – Communicating correct lifting to the workforce – Optimum class size – Equipment – Analogy of discs as shock absorbing springs – Demonstrating the "lever" principle of the spine. Motivating comments.

Part 2. The Ergonomics – Decide whether the operator should be seated or standing – Get the load off the floor – Male versus Female lifting characteristics – Minimise the distance the load is carried– Reduce the weight – Redesign the container – Use equipment for materials handling not operators – Any equipment must be easier than lifting physically – Utilise worker involvement.

Part 3. Hazard control programme – A major success story.

ACKNOWLEDGEMENTS

To my wife Polly, for correcting, retyping and editing the manuscript and for her many sound suggestions on what the average person might like to know about back injuries but is reluctant to ask.

To my son Ken, a talented freehand artist with a keen sense of humour, which he expressed very ably in many of the illustrations.

I am particularly indebted for the assistance I received from Mr O.R. Nicholson, O.B.E. F.R.C.S., F.R.A.C.S. a senior New Zealand orthopaedic surgeon and a good friend who devoted many hours to reviewing and editing the manuscript, and for his positive comments.

Also to Frank Bird Jr., former Director of the International Loss Control Institute, Loganville, Georgia, one of the world's great Safety Professionals, who first convinced me I should write this book.

Finally, I give credit for the work done by the many talented writers in this field, mentioning them in the text and references. If I have failed to do so adequately, I apologise.

FOREWORD

I have read Leonard Ring's latest book several times and I can recommend it to everyone who seeks to have a better understanding of their own and other people's backs.

Over the years I have read a large number of books on the back. Some of these have been detailed treatises on the anatomy and physiology of the spine, while others have detailed the non-surgical and surgical management of various problems. Others have been written for the general public. Many advocate, in an uncritical fashion, a particular line of treatment which will "cure" the person's symptoms.

The approach in this book is to explain, in an easily understood but not excessively oversimplified way, the reasons why some people develop bad backs. Certainly anything which can be done to reduce the incidence of back injuries is worthwhile. The cost to the community as a result of time lost from back injuries is enormous, quite apart from the impact on the person and their personal life from the restriction in their work and recreational activities. It is the management of the person with the painful back that is so important. They must understand the problem and its management, rather than trying to seek a "cure". A return to complete normality is the exception rather than the rule. Often those with acute back problems, by seeking early active treatment, actually prolong the problem by interfering with the natural history of the condition, which is for improvement over a period of several weeks. There is increasing evidence in the medical literature that even some of the most popular methods of treatment have no effect on this natural history.

For those with chronic back problems a "cure" is even more elusive. A large amount of money can be spent without any worthwhile results when, in a high proportion of cases, a careful study of a book such as this will enable the back sufferer to control their symptoms and where necessary, by modifying their work and recreational activities, continue to lead a productive life and enjoy their recreations.

ROSS NICHOLSON
O.B.E., F.R.C.S., F.R.A.C.S.
Consulting Auckland Orthopaedic Surgeon

INTRODUCTION

It is indeed a great pleasure for me to be able to write this introduction to Leonard Ring's new book. I am confident it will add enormously to the reputation of a man who has already become a legend in this field.

In was in 1975 when Leonard Ring arrived on the industrial safety scene with a simplified, research proven technique for lifting safely, that not only showed industry the control of back injuries was possible, but also a communication skill that was equally original and set new standards for seminar presentations. Many back schools, back rehabilitation centers and back injury prevention "specialists" in the U.S.A. and around the world today owe their success in part to the inspiration and techniques originally imparted through Leonard Ring's lectures and films.

We invited Mr Ring to lecture at the Loss Control Institute in Atlanta. As Director of the Institute, I immediately saw the Leonard Ring's approach to back injury prevention was unique, timely and urgent.

We persuaded him to make his first film "Bend Your Knees", which broke new ground for the comprehension and prevention of back injuries on film. It is still available in several languages, and continues to be the "classic" from which all other back films are evaluated.

Since then he has gone on to produce 14 video films on Ergonomics and Back Injury Control, culminating in a National Television campaign for his country in 1986 and the making of a documentary film "The Bad Back Video", which has been acclaimed as one of the most original back injury prevention films ever produced for general distribution.

Len Ring in "BACKS" brings a lifetime of experience to the problems associated with back injuries. His contribution to the field of Back Injury Control and Ergonomics from a professional and scientific standpoint has been enhanced by the addition of this new book, which has been meticulously researched and edited. Again, Len Ring has taken all the controversial issues surrounding back injury control and simplified them. I have often introduced him as one of the greatest living communicators on safety and health. I'm not sure that he isn't the greatest!

FRANK E BIRD JR.
President,
International Loss Control Institute,
Loganville, Georgia.

PREFACE

There must be more books on Backs than any other part of the human anatomy, so why write another one? My purpose is to record the best of my lecture material for my students, health professionals and back pain sufferers.

The facts and information presented at my seminars are not original; they have been around for years, but my experiences are, and what I have attempted to do here is to put them together in an interesting non-academic way, using the same language and style that characterises my lectures. There are also 150 illustrations and diagrams that I thought necessary to support my views, and added a touch of humour without detracting from the seriousness of the back problem.

I have always enjoyed communicating, both with my patients when I was in general physiotherapy practice and now as a lecturer and consultant. I well remember myself as a young student being fascinated by the magnificence of human anatomy and physiology, and wondering why it was not presented to us as an exciting adventure into the wonders of the human body.

It was not until Professor Bronowski did it so incredibly well in his memorable T.V. series on "The Ascent of Man", that I realised what enthusiasm and knowledge might do for a subject as mundane as back pain, vital though it was. His presentation made a lasting impression, and motivated me to try on a more humble level to also bridge this gap and bring a similar sense of excitement to my lectures and now in this book.

The format was given a great deal of ergonomic consideration, which is why it has an unconventional size and layout. The narrative is one side of the page and the proportional diagrams on the other, without the need to search other pages for the relevant illustration. On pages without illustrations the wide right margin was retained to provide space for notes.

Finally, the size of the letters should enable it to be read easily, even in poor light.

There are few conditions more exploited than back pain, with the doubtful exception of haemorrhoids. Early prevention, as with dental hygiene, requires it to be understood and pursued, so that the public can be spared the time and cost of the innumerable "cures" that they are persistently persuaded to purchase.

I hope the book will answer all the questions you did not have the opportunity to ask, and hopefully create or reinforce a commitment to take better care of your back.

For those who are reading my work for the first time, I hope it makes back pain and back injuries easier to understand and control.

LEONARD RING
M.Sc.(Erg.), F.Erg.Soc., M.C.S.P.(U.K.)
Auckland, New Zealand.

Chapter 1
THE FACTS ON BACKS

OBJECTIVES

I have three objectives; first, to convince you that you can control back injuries. I am not saying "cure", there is a very distinct difference, because back injuries are not a disease process. Second, to outline and demonstrate the method I advocate for the control and prevention of back injuries. Third, to give you personally an awareness of your own vulnerability in the area of back injuries and how you can avoid them. In this book, I offer no panacea, simply an awareness of back problems and their causes, their effects and their control.

I am assuming that many of my readers will be from various levels of management and supervision, or are people with back problems who wish to know the facts on backs however difficult it may be to accept, providing these facts are based on quantified research, experience and practical application. The practicality of proffered ideas and advice reflects one's personal experience in this area. There is no substitute for personal experience. I have spent the best part of the my life dealing with back injuries, both professionally and academically, not only in treatment and research, but also on the shop floor as an ergonomic consultant, specialising in back injury prevention and control.

I believe that to fully appreciate back injuries, both inside and outside of industry, you have to get your feet wet and your hands dirty. It is not a problem you can stand back from and

Doctors get it!

analyse by theory, saying this or that is the best way to control it. If you do, and the people to whom your advice is directed do not approve, the chances are they will say: "You try it!". And they are right! Try it for yourself and see how it feels after a few hours of repetitive lifting. It may then be a different matter. Many variables appear to complicate the "back" problem and it seems impossible to control, but, as we shall see, it can be done.

WHY IS IT ALWAYS BACKS?

Why worry so much about back injuries? There are many other important areas to concern us. More hand injuries occur than back injuries. People have burns. They fracture bones. Why don't we worry as much about those? The short answer is: hands get better, burns improve, fractures heal. But there is no end to the back injury. It is one of the most chronic sources of disability, both in and out of industry. Once you have had a back injury, it is three times easier to do it again. We do not classify a back injury as cured unless there has been no recurrence of symptoms for at least two years. The cost is horrendous and reads like a war reparations bill. Over the whole spectrum of industrial injuries, only one type, the back injury, appears to be increasing in number and cost.

No one is immune. You may never have suffered a back injury or back pain – I hope you haven't – and might, therefore, be thinking that this doesn't apply to you personally. But if you are over thirty, your chances are one in three that some day – and it could be tomorrow – you are going to get out of bed as usual, walk into the bathroom, the kitchen, or your office or factory, bend down unthinkingly to pick something up off the floor, or tie your shoelaces, something you have done a thousand times before... and as you bend, a sudden stab of pain will rip through your back making you immobile within a few hours, or worse still, immediately.

The slightest movement will be agony, even breathing deeply will be acutely painful, as it increases the pressure within the spinal canal and you will be a mixture of fear, pain and sweat, at a loss to understand what has hit you. After all, you've been doing this every day for years. Without any apparent cause or warning you have joined an army of back sufferers. Welcome to the club!

Unfortunately back pain, more than any other physical problem, has for so long been associated with industrial malingering and pseudo psychosomatic diagnoses that it is likely to receive only token sympathy from friends and colleagues alike. The response invariably is to keep silent and live with it.

STAGGERING STATISTICS

Fact 1. If you were offered a bag of sugar coated sweets and informed at the same time that three of the four of those sweets were, in fact, coated with a substance that would put you in great pain and might limit your activities for ever, I am sure you would not only refuse to take any, but would put the jar in a place that was safely away from your family. But that is precisely the odds of getting a back injury in your lifetime, and it is not very comforting.

Fact 2. Historically, the back problem is not a recent acquisition to our civilisation. The ancient Egyptians diagnosed sciatica about 5000 years ago (Finneson), and in New Zealand, a 3000 year old Egyptian Mummy was X-rayed and found to have marked degeneration of all the lumbar vertebrae (Ring, L. 1988).

Fact 3. Perhaps we walked upright too soon! Animals don't seem to get bad backs? The answer is "Yes". Some animals do suffer from degenerative back problems, despite their posture, notably Dachshunds, Alsatians and German Shepherds, who tend to develop spinal stenosis. This is a condition of narrowing of the spinal canal which houses the spinal cord. There may be subsequent compression and hind limb paralysis. (Nachemson 1975)

Fact 4. Incidence of Back Injuries
U.S.A. estimate 7 million cases per year (Time, July 1980)
U.K. estimate 70,000 cases in 1981 (H. and S. Exec.Doc.)
Aust. estimate 30,000 cases in 1979 (Bureau of Lab.Stat.)
N.Z. estimate 26,000 cases in 1989 (N.Z.Acc.Comp.Corp.)

Fact 5. Cost Annually in Money and Workdays.
U.S.A. estimate – $5 billion – 93 million (Time, July 1980)
U.K. estimate – £50 million – 31 million (D. of H. and Safety)
Aust. estimate – $170 million – 1 million (OSH.Dep.Labour)

Fact 6. Cost per case (U.S.A.)
Current estimates: Mean cost = $5,739 (Snook, S. 1987)

Fact 7. Average age (U.S.A.)
Males 34. Female 35 (Klein et al).

The National Safety Council reports that for the years 1980-1990, 25% of all compensable injuries in the U.S.A. resulted from manual materials handling with over 65% involving the spine. Estimated compensation and medical payments alone are in excess of 14 billion dollars annually.

Great Britain
In Great Britain, the time lost through back injuries is estimated to be more than twice the time lost through strikes; 18 million work days compared with 9.3 million work days lost through strikes. The time alone cost more than £700 million or $U.S.1,680 million. In 1978, over £90 million or $U.S.216 million was paid in Social Security payments and

£60 million ($U.S.144 million) paid out in drugs. On any one day in Great Britain, 10,000 insured persons will have been off work with back pain for six months or more, and 45% of these incapacitated for two years. Almost 41,000 people, (0.1% of the population), will be admitted to hospitals with back trouble, more than half as planned admissions, and over 3,300 will undergo surgical treatment. One in every five accidents in Great Britain is either directly or indirectly back-related.

Economists may say that Great Britain's problem is its industrial unrest, but the economic cost of back injuries is equally devastating. It is estimated to be equal to losing the total population output of a town (like Norwich) for one year. (Jayson, M.I.V. "The Lumbar Spine and Back Pain" 1980).

New Zealand
In New Zealand, claims for back injuries on the Accident Compensation scheme for the last five years have totalled 130,135 at a cost of $771,524,701. This represents an increase of 21.8% in claims and 28.5% in compensation paid. A high price for such a small country to endure.

Australia
In Australia, The Bureau of Statistics reports that in 1986, there were 32,987 manual handling accidents, resulting in a loss to industry of 412,661 working weeks at a cost of $A.166, 169,900.

THE HUMAN FACE OF STATISTICS

It is important not to let the statistics numb you to the human cost. Every number is a face, every face a thinking, feeling, hoping human being. We make the statistics.

I have seen workers with a chronic back problem become increasingly anti-social as they see their job security threatened by an environment of mass unemployment and redundancy.

Approximately 15% of all back injuries end in a permanent chronic disability. A chronic back is not some mild nagging discomfort. It is someone with a permanent level of pain, to whom everything becomes a calculated risk, like playing with the children, a round of golf, or bending down to take the roast out of the oven. You may get away with it, but you may not. Confidence is eroded, and job security is threatened. Of course, people do not get fired for having a bad back, but when there are things you can't do anymore, you begin looking over your shoulder to see who is noticing.

Four times as many back injuries occur off-the-job as on-the-job. 80% of the world's population have had a back injury or been a victim of back pain at some time in their lives, and studies indicate that towards the end of a normal life span the prevalence of at least some degree of disc degeneration is almost 100%.

Somewhere at this moment a person is working at a bench or desk, who will never be the same twenty-four hours from now. Some houseperson is about to bend down to take a dish out of a badly designed oven, and may never be able to do it again without pain. Sure it doesn't kill, but it gives most of us who get it the feeling that it might, and the tragedy is that it could have been prevented.

Chapter 2

IT'S NOT WHAT YOU LIFT

You may have had enough of statistics, and I shall finish with them, but I know no other way to set the scene and show the urgency of the problem. It is a tragedy to the human condition compounded by the fact that we now know how back injuries occur, we know why they occur, and we know how to minimise them. The frustrating thing is that it is so simple. Injuring your spine, or having a high incidence of industrial back injuries today can be considered as ignorance of the known facts.

DISEASE VERSUS DEGENERATION

The main difficulty is that we are not dealing with a disease in the germ or bacterial sense. The sufferer is not ill, with loss of appetite and a high temperature. I wish this were the situation; if so, we could deal with it more easily. We have antibiotics now which can kill almost anything — including the patient occasionally! Unfortunately, what we are dealing with is a process called "degeneration", the medical term for "**wear** and **tear**".

The basic elements creating "wear and tear" are weight, plus time, plus friction. It means that everything wears out eventually; nothing lasts forever, the spine being no exception. The fact that you cannot see this taking place makes no difference to its reality.

The degeneration, or wear and tear process, is accelerated by

Fig. 1. Occupational postures contribute to back problems.

Fig. 2. Car designs contribute to back problems. The degenerative process is accelerated by lifting and carrying in badly designed cars.

Fig. 3. The average person bolts and unbolts doors a thousands times a year putting his or her back at risk each time.

lifting and carrying, and the poor posture involved in many day-to-day activities. What do I mean by poor occupational posture? Well, a job which forces the operator to stoop all day (Fig. 1) is poor occupational posture. Lifting something and putting it in the trunk of some cars is positively hazardous for backs (Fig. 2). The average houseperson bolting and unbolting a door, often at floor level, perhaps a thousand times a year is another example of poor occupational posture.

There is no reason for a door bolt to be at ground level (Fig.3). Each time it is operated, it is at the risk of a back injury, particularly as people get older, their muscles get weaker and their joints stiffen. If it was 18 inches (460mm.) higher, there would be only one third of the possibility of suffering a back injury.

Frankly, as a lecturer in Ergonomics at the University School of Architecture, I cannot understand why, in view of the accepted wisdom on back physiology, bolts are still fixed to the bottom of doors, electric power outlets are almost at floor level and garden taps are difficult to reach. A questionnaire of 6,000 policy holders from Liberty Mutual Insurance indicated that 66% of all industrial lifting tasks start below waist level, but these low lifting tasks were associated with 78% of lifting injuries.

One of the problems with designers is that some think the world is made up of young athletic, goodlooking, intelligent designers. In fact, one-third of the population are like me, with reduced strength, mobility, vision and hearing. Must we live with, and be injured by equipment and buildings because the designers tend to ignore physical limitations, such as height or reach, or the physiological changes produced simply by a relentless ageing process?

We will return to work postures in due course, but the worst factor by far for accelerating wear and tear on the spine is due to lifting and carrying. A first response to the term "lifting and carrying" is to imagine a heavy weight being lifted and moved, but it may not have occurred to you that, when you bend to tie your shoelaces, straighten up and walk away, you have lifted the weight of your trunk. In an average adult of approx. 5'8" (1.78mm) this is about 100lbs (45kg), and is greater than any weight you would normally be expected to lift. Indeed, if someone gave you a 98lb (44kg) sack of cement and asked you to carry it around all day, you wouldn't last five minutes. Yet that is what you are demanding from your spine every second you spend standing or sitting. It is only relieved when you lie down.

Added to that, as soon as you commence to bend in any direction, the cantilever action of the spine makes the weight of the trunk significantly greater, compounding the stress. From this point of view, therefore, the term "lifting and carrying" becomes synonymous with "bending and stretching".

The trunk itself, by its sheer weight and flexibility, is central to the problem; whatever weight is lifted, must simply be added to the burden of the weight of an already mechanically disadvantaged trunk. The spine was not designed to function like a crane; there are ways of bending and stretching that are easy, yet safe, minimising the risk of injury.

PRIMITIVE MAN VERSUS MODERN MAN

Of course, the spine was designed to bend and stretch, but it was not designed to last for three score years and ten, without showing signs of wear and tear, anymore than we were designed to spend a majority of our lives outside of work, sitting to watch T.V., sitting to eat, sitting in cars or sitting on the toilet, with our muscles getting soft and losing condition.

Adding to that, the amount of bending and lifting in present day society is enormously greater than in pre-neolithic times; 500 lifts per day by 20th century man, compared with 50 lifts a day by primitive man. Archaeological evidence suggests that pre-neolithic life expectancy was about 40 years, an understandable statistic; for as soon as a warrior's physical condition diminished and he could no longer fight or hunt with the same efficiency, wild animals or warring tribes made quite sure that he was not around for very much longer.

Modern man lives to approximately 75 years; modern woman approximately 78 years. If you are a male reading this book and have reached 75, make a will; every day is a bonus! Longevity, and the wear and tear associated with that longevity must take its toll, whether it is heart, lungs, kidneys, or spine. The problem of back pain in the same context is really the problem of a spine unable to match a lifestyle of continual bending and lifting. One of the dilemmas of modern medicine is that, having resolved most of the fatal diseases of childhood and adolescence, it faces the problems of an ageing society with limited surgical replacement techniques. Because of the proximity of the spinal cord, replacing the spine is still a long way off.

It may be Utopian, but the objective of designers should be to design lifting entirely out of the work environment.
That, and training people to bend correctly, are the basic principles on which successful back injury prevention must be based, whether on a National, Corporate or individual level.

One large railway workshop in the U.S.A. reduced its back injuries by 75% in one year with the simple expedient of taking everything on the floor up to a working height of 18 inches. (450mm).

However, you can instruct an operator how to lift correctly every day, but if the work space is such that he or she cannot get close enough to the load to do it correctly, or if the weight lifted is beyond the normal limitations of the spine, you are just wasting their time and yours. What is worse, the advice appears ridiculous.

In the last few years, research into back injuries has been significant, but sadly the researchers tend to speak a language only fellow researchers understand. To the people who really need it – the sufferers, the supervisors, and the Safety Managers – it sounds like a plethora of words. They buy numerous books on the subject, which have a tendency to be either over-simplistic or academically complex, and end up buying more books to explain the original ones.

In today's factories, houses, and institutions, people are continually bending, stretching, straining, growing older, and wearing out.

The average home is a minefield (Fig. 4) for injuring the back. Look anywhere and you will find unnecessary back stress situations imposed by equipment or product designs that ignores basic spinal mechanics, or known ergonomic data on back injury prevention.

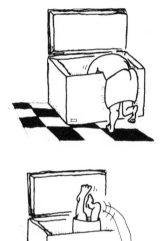

Fig. 4. The average home is a minefield.

11

Chapter 3
GENESIS

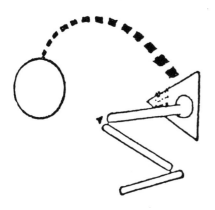

Fig. 5. The foetal curve.

Back problems begin the day you are born. Let us assume you have just arrived. You will emerge with your spine shaped like a large letter "C" (Fig. 5). At this stage, in a manner of speaking, it is like a piece of rubber, flexible but with no stability. Your centre of gravity is well in front, and when you are carried, your head and trunk must be supported or you will collapse.

MILESTONE ONE

Within the next twelve months or so, you will duplicate man's greatest achievement, that is to stand up and walk! In one year, your spine will pass through millions of years of human evolution.

The first objective is to control the movements of the head. One good reason for this is the necessity to see where you're going. It is achieved by a clever arrangement of powerful muscles at the back of neck, which are larger and more numerous than those in front. Consequently, they develop at a much faster rate and quickly overcome the instability of gravity and the weight of the head. Constant stimuli from the sounds and sights around you enhances this development and within about three months of this activity, the neck muscles develop sufficient "tone" to hold the head upright and bring the head and neck under independent control.

"Muscle Tone" refers to the inherent tension within all

13

healthy muscles and is a measure of the degree of that tension. The fitter the muscle, the better will be its tension or "tone". This is very evident in body builders whose muscles look tensed even when they are relaxed.

The tightening of the posterior neck muscles results in the formation of a small secondary "C" curve going in the opposite direction to the large original curve (Fig. 6) with which you began this journey. It is called the "cervical lordosis." Well done! Your head is now under your control and you have accomplished your first milestone!

Although largely instinctive, you nevertheless have to work at maintaining this curve throughout your life; for instance, lose concentration or get drowsy and nod off in front of television, the first thing that drops is your head.

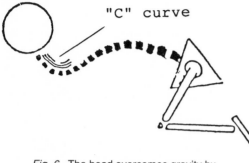

"C" curve

Fig. 6. The head overcomes gravity by the development of the posterior neck muscles.

MILESTONE TWO

This segment of the spine is now stable and you can be lifted up without the need for supporting the head. However, the rest of the trunk is till unstable and continues to need outside assistance for support.

The lower trunk is a much larger and heavier mass than the upper trunk, and it therefore takes longer to strengthen and develop, even though the principles that determine this development remains the same. The mechanics are similar; the muscles in the lumbar area being larger and, therefore, potentially stronger than the thin sheet of abdominal muscles in front, strengthen and develop their "tone". They too contract and pull the spine backwards, opening up the lumbar segment to produce another reversed "C" curve, similar to the neck area. It is known as the "lumbar lordosis," just as the curve in the neck has become the "cervical lordosis" (Fig. 7).

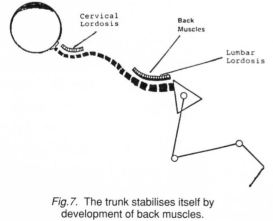

Cervical Lordosis

Back Muscles

Lumbar Lordosis

Fig.7. The trunk stabilises itself by development of back muscles.

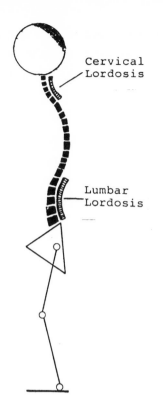

Fig.8. The upright posture.

With continuous exercise in which crawling plays an important part, the back muscles continue to develop and eventually become strong enough to maintain your trunk permanently in its upright posture. It will have taken you twelve to fifteen months, but you will now instinctively climb up anything available — chairs, doors, walls, or your own knees — in order to stand up and view the world from this new position. Of course, you will occasionally fall down, because your centre of gravity takes time to adjust itself to this drastic change, but once started, within a few months it will become permanent. You do not walk because running is easier. Walking demands a higher level of balance and co-ordination than running. In any event, congratulations! You've made it, welcome to the human race (Fig. 8).

Naturally, there are other factors without which the upright posture is impossible. At the risk of oversimplification, I have discussed only the more important elements, so that mechanics of the stress produced by bending and stretching will be seen in perspective.

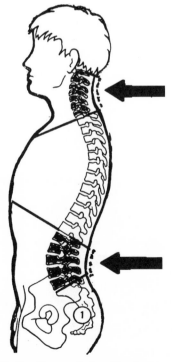

Fig.9a. The cervical and lumbar spine is the fulcrum for bending.

THE COST

Unfortunately, there are no free lunches! A price must be paid for standing upright. The price is that, because the area of the back between the neck and lower back known as the "thoracic" segment holds the ribcage with most of the vital organs, its movements are somewhat limited and designed more for rotation. It is therefore, almost exclusively in the region of the two secondary curves that flexion and extension of the spine takes place. The cervical and lumbar spine thus becomes the "fulcrum" or centre for most spinal movement, in particular bending and stretching, or in other words, lifting. (Fig.9a)

The fulcrum is the point about which a lever turns in lifting a body; it is also the point of greatest friction and, conse-

15

quently, the area of greatest wear and tear, and explains why degeneration is almost always confined to these areas (Fig. 9b).

We have discussed wear and tear as a product of time, plus weight, plus friction, and although degeneration is relatively common in the cervical spine, it is minor compared to the lumbar spine which has to carry the weight of the entire trunk, including the head, for approximately "three score years and ten."

Merely standing is a gymnastic feat akin to the Eiffel Tower without a base, and is only possible because of the wonderful mobility of the lumbar spine. It should, therefore, come as no surprise that 75% of the entire adult population have lower back problems or "syndromes" at some time or other in their lives.

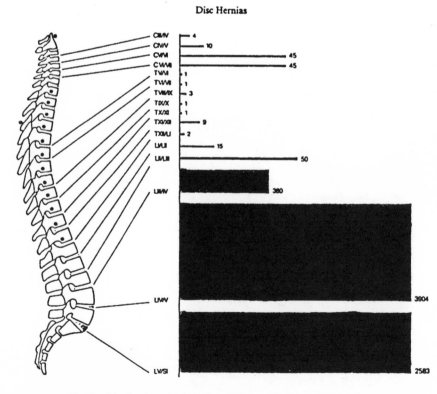

Fig.9b. Distribution of 7,054 disc lesions at Zurich Neurological Clinic shows 97% (6,787) occured in the lumbar region.

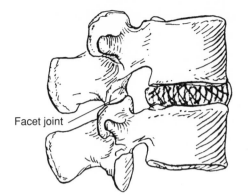

Facet joint

Fig.10. Functional units and facet joints.

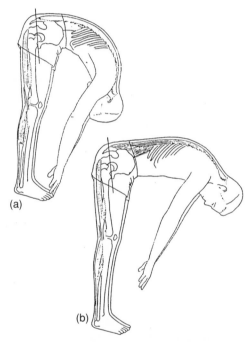

(a)

(b)

Fig.11. (a) Normal range of monvement.
(b) Possible effect of degenerative change.

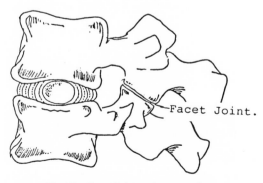

Facet Joint.

Fig.12. Facet joint, note narrowing.

Chapter 4
STRUCTURE OF THE SPINE

The spine is made up of a number of superimposed vertebrae (Fig. 10.), each of which forms a self-contained functional unit. Although the range of movement of the whole spine is very large, it is really quite small between any two segments, and it is only when multiplied by the total number of vertebrae does it achieve its remarkable range. Because of this, any loss of movement between two or three vertebrae resulting from age or disease, may not seriously affect the functional range of movement. Indeed, the loss of mobility in the lumbar spine of the elderly may be quite significant but pass unnoticed, due to trunk flexion and extension being transferred to the hip joints and upper back. (Fig. 11)

The front part of each unit is designed for weight-bearing and shock absorbing functions, as indicated by its relatively massive structure. Movement here is minimal. The functional movement occurs to the back of the vertebrae in what are known as the "facet joints" (Fig. 12). The structure of these joints is interesting and crucial to back function.

Despite their small size, about 1/2" in diameter, their structure is identical to larger joints, like the hip or shoulder, and is characterised by having its own lubricating system and producing its own oil called synovial fluid which cannot be synthesised. The facet joints are an example of human structural engineering at its very best, and if you could look inside, you would see adjoining surfaces that are smooth, glisten, and tougher than the dentine on your teeth. This hardness ensures that friction and wear and tear is reduced to a minimum.

The space between the adjoining surfaces of the facet joints is extremely narrow with a critical tolerance (see Fig. 12 again). It follows that any change in the relationship of the disc space in front will increase the pressure and, therefore, friction on the surface of the facet joints behind, leading to an erosion or "flaking off" of the joint surface.

What is created now is a cycle of accelerated wear and tear, increased friction, followed by more wear and tear, with a consequent inflammatory reaction, producing pain, muscle spasm and loss of function. In many degenerative back conditions, this is the site of "Lumbago", with perhaps later involvement of the nerve roots, which then becomes "Sciatica".

Obviously, the prevention of non-pathological back pain must be centred on the mechanics of maintaining a normal disc space between the vertebrae. Unfortunately, this can be difficult, for as we shall see later, discs as they age, tend to get thinner.

In a manner of speaking, the vertebrae is a series of individual joints, which function as a whole like the joints of the ankle or the knee. Joints must be protected from strain and held in their correct alignment to enable the attached muscles to contract and pull the joint into its elected position.

The function is carried out in the first instance by muscles which contract to initiate the movement, and in the second, by ligaments which holds the joint together. Therefore, providing there is no joint dysfunction, it is the muscles and ligaments which, not only determine the range of movement of joints, but also by their strength and fitness protect them against injury. (Fig.13a)

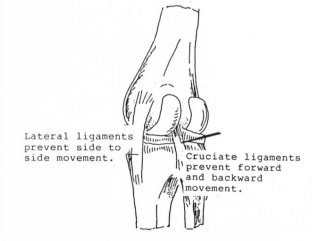

Lateral ligaments prevent side to side movement.

Cruciate ligaments prevent forward and backward movement.

Fig. 13a. Ligaments of the knee are taut, strong structures that determine the range and stability of the joints preventing dislocation.

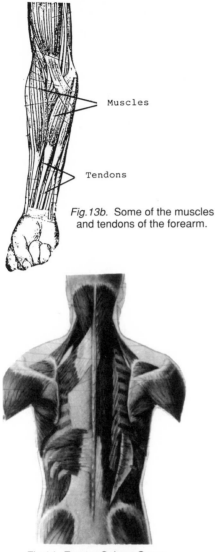

Fig.13b. Some of the muscles and tendons of the forearm.

Muscles

Tendons

Fig.14. Erector Spinae Group.

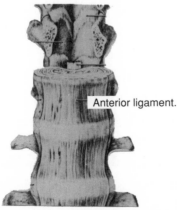

Anterior ligament.

Fig.15. Anterior ligament.

It needs to be understood that muscles and ligaments are two distinctly separate structures with specialised functions. Muscle is an elastic tissue, whose function is to shorten, (contract) and extend (stretch), thereby moving the bones (the levers) via the joints. With the exception of specialised functions like the face or eyes, most skeletal muscles are attached to bones, with the muscle spanning the joint between them. Generally, most voluntary muscles are not inserted directly into bone, but rather through the medium of a strong tough, non-elastic cordlike structure called a tendon. Tendons may vary in length from a fraction of an inch to more than a foot. (Fig.13b)

In the spine, the muscles consist of a system of several layers of short and long muscle strands which have the task of supporting and moving the spine. They are attached to the bony prominences of the vertebrae and the ribs, and play an important part in maintaining the shape of the spinal column. Their name, the "Erector Spinae" group describes their function. (Fig.14.)

The ligaments are taut, non-elastic, but nevertheless flexible material, very much like the rigging holding up the mast of a sailing ship, or the guy ropes supporting a flagpole. In the spine, they are massive structures with a breaking strain of approximately 2,000lbs. to the square inch, running like a pair of steel cables in front and behind the bodies of the vertebrae. They hold all the segments together, supporting and reinforcing the spine, restricting excessive movement and the tendency to any shearing action.

In front (anteriorly), the ligament is broad, extensive, and firmly attached, indeed, welded to the surfaces of the vertebrae all the way down. It is one of the limiting factors in bending the spine backwards (Fig. 15).

At the back (posteriorly), it begins quite broad, but narrows

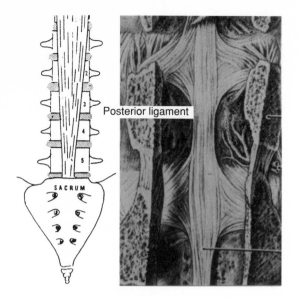

Fig.16. Posterior ligament in the lumbar segment.

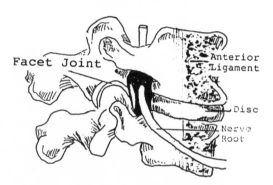

Fig.17. The nerve root passes downward and forward in close proximity to the unprotected disc.

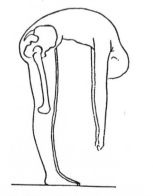

Fig.18. The spine is not a crane.

markedly as it approaches the bottom of the spine. At the level of the fourth or fifth lumbar vertebrae, it has reduced to less than half its original width, exposing unprotected disc on either side (Fig.16). The lumbar discs, therefore, particularly the fourth and fifth are not fully protected by ligament, and are more likely to be subject to structural weaknesses.

An extremely important observation must now be drawn. It is that this portion of the back, which acts as the fulcrum for the trunk in flexion and extension, is the recipient of most of the stress, but has less ligamentous support than any other portion of the spine. Its supporting strength is derived from a narrow, apparently deficient posterior ligament and whatever passes for back muscles.

The vulnerability of this area is further compounded by nerve roots emerging from either side of the vertebrae to pass down and across this unprotected portion of the discs (Fig.17).

Therefore, in bending forward, it must be evident that the spine becomes analogous to a crane but without its structural support, and attempts to use it in this way by picking things up from the floor or putting them down with straight legs using the back, is putting stresses on the spine, for which it was not designed (Fig.18).

It is for these reasons that degenerative changes, associated with lowered resistance, is so prevalent in the lumbar spine and, consequently, why it is the site of so much pain. We now need to look at the changes in the mechanics of the spine imposed by this degeneration to understand some of the reasons for back pain. It begins with its anatomical components.

Chapter 5

THE DISC

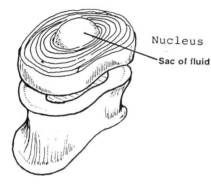

Fig.19. The disc looks like a series of concentric onion rings with a sac of fluid in the centre.

It is a pity medicine ever coined the word "disc" for the wonderful shock-absorbing system between the vertebrae. It has resulted in such misconception and confusion that any rationale for pain seems plausible. Ridiculous T.V. commercials insult our intelligence, compounding the insult with irrelevant and unsupported psuedo-scientific facts.

Fig.20. Annulus Fibrosis. The angles of the annulus elastic fibres vary from horizontal to oblique to perpendicular.

THE DISC, "STRUCTURE"

The disc is not a "disc". It is not something round and flat, looking like a frisbee. It is more like the inner tube of a car tyre, but oval in shape (Fig. 19), consisting of an outer core of layers of elastic-bands lying in the same plane but at varying angles from horizontal to oblique, to almost perpendicular at the outer edge. They criss cross and intertwine and are smaller in diameter at the top. If you were to cut one in half transversely, it would have the appearance of a series of concentric onion rings (Fig. 20). It is called the "annulus fibrosus", which simply means circular fibres.

The centre of the annulus fibrosis is filled with a sac of jelly-like substance, which is 88% water. The material in the sac is so compressed that an internal pressure is generated high enough to burst it were it not for the strength and elasticity of the annular fibres that surround it. The sac is called the "nucleus pulposus", or more descriptively, spongy centre. (Fig.21).

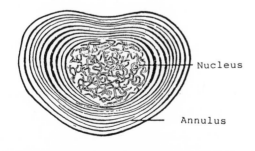

Fig.21. Disc cross-section. The disc looking from the top consists of layers of elastic-like bands surrounding an inner sac of fluid (gel).

The outer layer, or annulus fibrosis is welded to the corre-

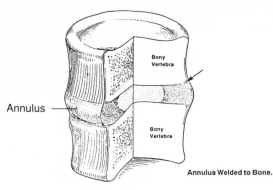

Fig.22. Annulus welded to bone. The outer layer of fibrous bands (annulus) is completely welded to the bony vertebrae above and below.

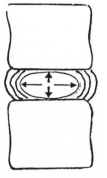

Fig.23. Pressure is distributed evenly throughout the disc.

sponding vertebrae above and below, and is almost indistinguishable from the bone (Fig.22), making the term "slipped disc" nonsense and, as we shall see later, simply a play on words. Discs do not "slip" in the way most laymen and more than a few health professionals imagine.

THE DISC "FUNCTION"

The disc functions as a hydraulic shock absorber, much the same way as a pair of motorcycle forks. Owners of pre-World War II motorcycles will remember, without nostalgia, the fixed front forks of those early bonecrushers. Others may remember vintage tractor seats without springs, and what they felt like. We now know such machines were associated with a high incidence of early disc degeneration.

All the mechanical principles of hydraulics are utilised in the human spine. The nucleus, which is incompressible, invests the disc with a dynamic function. This allows it to re-distribute pressures evenly in a centrifugal manner through the elastic fibres of the surrounding annulus. As a result, vertical pressures are re-directed in a radical direction like the spokes of a wheel (Fig. 23). Compression of the spine, or jarring associated with running and jumping, can therefore be absorbed.

Because of gravity and bodyweight in the upright position, whether sitting or standing, it is obvious that the disc must always be under some sort of tension due to the compression force being generated by this posture.

It is not often appreciated that, whatever force is applied to the disc from any direction, the nucleus or inner sac does not move, but is simply squeezed, which propels its jelly-like substance away from the pressure to where there will be less resistance. The result of this is to change the shape of the inner sac, whilst the elastic outer fibres stretch to accommo-

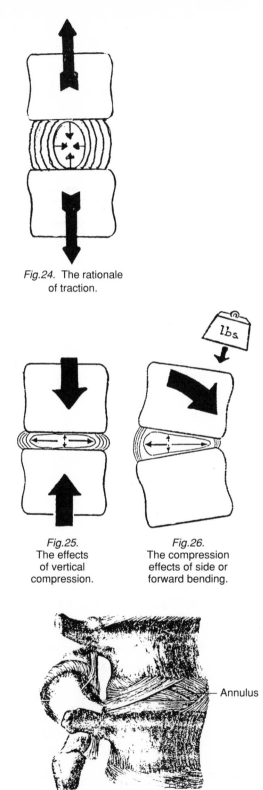

Fig.24. The rationale
of traction.

Fig.25.
The effects
of vertical
compression.

Fig.26.
The compression
effects of side or
forward bending.

— Annulus

Fig.27. Fibres of the annulus that
assist to limit specific disc rotation.

date it. Thus, changes of pressure within the disc are opposed and controlled, allowing the disc to resume its original status quo relationship when the pressure returns to normal.

If the spine is elongated and the discs pulled apart, the nucleus which was flatter at rest, now becomes more spherical and the annulus increases its tension. There is an increase in disc height which results in a reduction of internal pressure. This is the rationale for traction as a conservative treatment in some types of back injury. (Fig. 24.)

On the other hand, if the spine is compressed by jumping or bending, the nucleus becomes flatter and wider, increasing its internal pressure (Fig. 25). The pressure is then transmitted to the inner-most fibres of the annulus, which now stretch in a lateral direction to control it. If the spine is bent forward, the fluid can only be squeezed backward. Whatever the movement, the nucleus is forced in the opposite direction away from the compression in order to stabilise the system. (Fig. 26)

Nothing demonstrates the ingenuity of the disc for self-preservation better than the movement of rotation. Here, the most oblique fibres of the annulus, which run in the direction of the movement, are stretched, whilst the fibres going in the opposite direction are relaxed in a scissors-like action (Fig. 27). Unfortunately, this action is also accompanied by a great build up of tension in the nucleus, because the most oblique of these fibres are adjacent to the nucleus itself (Fig. 28). Bending and twisting, particularly with a weight, can be hazardous and the high percentage of back injuries related specifically to this movement supports this fact.

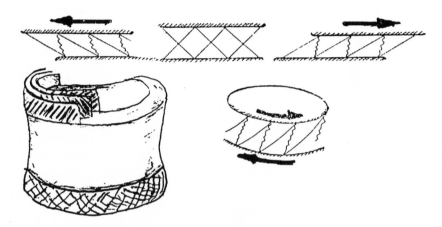

Fig.28. Scissors action of annulus fibres in rotation.

THE "SLIPPED DISC"

The prolapse or rupture of an inter-vertebral disc is perhaps the most recognised spinal problem. Research indicates that only a previously degenerated or worn disc will rupture through its protective annulus. In other words, a disc would have to be abnormal to make a prolapse possible. This is what makes the term "slipped disc" misleading and dangerous. It is dangerous because it conveys a false idea of the underlying pathology, implying that symptoms arise because a disc "slips out", and that all will be well by the disc slipping back in again. Let us set this straight. Discs do not slip, they may prolapse, herniate, or rupture, which is probably what it is intended to convey, but they do not slip.

Nevertheless, the term continues to be used with reckless abandon, conditioning thousands of people to an idea that they have something akin to a dislocated spine. The psychological problems that such a loose diagnosis produces are often much worse than the original condition, and inevitably handicaps the period of rehabilitation.

The possibility of healthy discs prolapsing or rupturing as a result of lifting is very remote. Investigation on patients who have died from sudden vertical injuries, like parachutists or high rise construction workers, has shown that the sudden compression force has virtually burst through the bodies of the vertebrae in an upward and downward direction, while the elastic outer bands of the annulus have remained intact. Obviously, the annulus is tough enough to withstand such pressures. Experiments have shown that normal healthy discs will not rupture in any other manner.

THE DISC "DEFENCES"

The disc has an indepth defence system that is quite formidable. First, the powerful muscles of the spine. Second, the ligament and third, the inherent strength of the annulus welded between the bodies of the vertebrae. Consider what would have to take place to prolapse a disc in the absence of existing degeneration. The first response to impending injury is a split second reflex contraction of the muscles. It happens so fast it defies the imagination, mainly because this kind of action is an instinctive self-preservation response to danger. Our survival depends a great deal on speed, and we have devised a method of by-passing the brain on such occasions, letting the spinal cord do the thinking for itself. We call it a "reflex" muscle action.

For a disc to rupture as a result of traumatic injury, you would have to tear the muscles before this protective spasm or contraction occurs. This is possible, but improbable. However, even if you succeed, you then meet the second line of defence, the ligaments. The injury now has to be severe enough to tear these, and we have already discussed their strength. If the injury is severe enough to do that, you reach the third line of defence – the disc itself, which, you may remember, is welded to the bony vertebrae to a degree that makes it more likely you would fracture a vertebra before you would tear it away from its attachments to the spine.

THE "SLIPPED DISC" FINIS

Let me quote Grays Anatomy, the classic anatomical text, for the most authoritative last word. It says, (p. 486, 33rd.Ed.): "In the young adult, the intervertebral discs are so strong that, when violence is applied to the vertebral column, the bones give way first, providing the discs are healthy". In other words, the force would have to be great enough to cleave the vertebra in two, which would then obviously include damage to the discs, and is about as rare as the proverbial hen's teeth.

The only exception described by Grays is in the cervical region (neck), where "through forced flexion (forward bending of the head and neck), rupture of a disc may occur without a prior fracture". This is of course the classic description of a "whiplash" type injury, where a ballistic-like movement beyond control is likely to tear the muscles, then the ligaments, and then perhaps pry a small piece of disc from its anchored position. This is why a true "whiplash" injury can be so painful.

However, this refers to the cervical spine which is the neck area, not the lumbar spine. The lumbar discs and vertebrae are anchored to the pelvis, which in turn is anchored by the legs. They are not subject to the amplitude of a vibratory injury such as occurs in the neck. The lumbar area is also far too strong and massive to allow for a "whiplash" type injury. Like many things, it is only theoretically possible.

The spine is truly a magnificent example of structural

engineering. Consider its specifications:-

1. *It must be able to carry the weight of the human trunk.*

2. *It must be flexible to allow bending and rotation in all directions under heavy load.*

3. *It must be hollow to allow delicate nerves and blood vessels to pass through it and emerge without being damaged by movement.*

4. *It must function adequately for a lifetime.*

In summary, it is no exaggeration to say that your upright posture is maintained by a structure with the strength of a box girder due to the specialised construction of the vertebra, the stability of a suspension bridge due to its ligaments, and the flexibility of a coiled steel spring due to its massive musculature.

Why then, when the spine is such a remarkable piece of engineering does it apparently wear out so early? To see this in perspective, we need to look more definitively at the dynamics of its function.

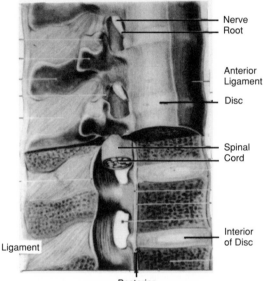

Nerve Root

Anterior Ligament

Disc

Spinal Cord

Interior of Disc

Ligament

Posterior Ligament

Chapter 6
DEGENERATION

It is an immutable physical law that perpetual motion is impossible, and that most things eventually wear out or stop. We recognise this fact and accept it in relation to our environment and ourselves, and are not surprised to look in the mirror and see our hair getting thinner, wrinkles appearing, teeth disappearing and muscles beginning to sag. But, of course, everything else wears at the same rate, the fact that you cannot see it is no criteria — the list includes heart, lungs, kidneys and yes, the spine.

However, the way things wear out generally follows a pattern that is related to its function. By that, I mean the chair you are sitting on to read this will inevitably become ricketty and unstable, or the upholstery will get ragged. The light with which you may be reading this book will, in time, burn out. We are not surprised at this, yet it is difficult for people to accept the concept with regard to their discs, despite the fact that they must also be subject to the same physical laws.

We must be concerned with the physiology of disc function next, if the process of degeneration is to be understood.

IN THE NUCLEUS

Two essential factors need to be considered; the first is, the nucleus is a permeable sac similar to the structure of a muslin bag. Therefore, if the pressure within the sac rises, some of the

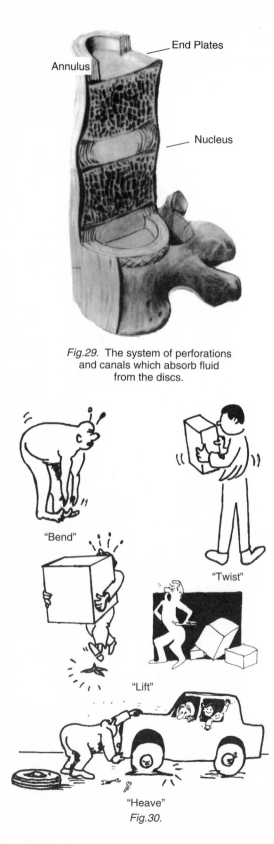

Fig.29. The system of perforations and canals which absorb fluid from the discs.

fluid content can be squeezed by osmosis through the membrane that holds it. The second is a question. In view of the fact that the disc is welded between two vertebrae where does the fluid go? The answer is, into the bone itself.

If you could look at the top or bottom of any single vertebra (they are called the "end plates") through a microscope, you would see myriads of tiny perforations; these perforations continue through the vertebrae to form a system of canals that constitutes its interior structure (Fig. 29).

Fluid from the nucleus is, therefore, able to be absorbed into the body of the vertebra when pressure in the sac rises, albeit in microscopic amounts. This facility is part of the shock absorbing function of discs.

Movements of the spine subject the nucleus to constant change, compressing and relaxing the disc like a sponge. From bending and stretching countless times a day, often with weights far above human tolerances to bending, twisting, pushing, pulling, holding and heaving (Fig. 30), the continuous increase and decrease in pressure forces fluid out of the sac to be absorbed through the microscopic perforations in the vertebra above and below the disc. The consequent loss of disc height can reduce overall stature at the end of a day by anything up to 1/2" (12.5mm) (Fig. 31).

During sleep, the compressive force generated by gravity and body weight is minimal; the water absorbing capacity of the

"Bend"

"Twist"

"Lift"

"Heave"

Fig.30.

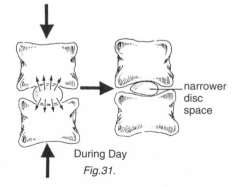

narrower disc space

During Day

Fig.31.

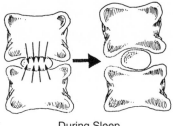

During Sleep

Fig.32.

nucleus now has an opportunity to draw its fluid back into the sac, the disc regains its original size, and intra-discal relationships are normalised (Fig. 32). Undoubtably, we are shorter at night than in the morning!

As we get older, the wearing process is reflected in our inability to manufacture the materials essential to the body's needs at the rate they are diminishing. Hair is not forever, nor are teeth nor hormones, connective tissue, and many other important but not life threatening materials. Suffer a fracture in old age and it may never heal properly, because there may not be enough calcium produced, and a metal plate to hold the bone ends together could be the only recourse.

Similarly, ageing slows down the discs' dynamic process of recovery. The ability to make up the fluid loss in the nucleus after a good night's sleep diminishes because less fluid is produced, and the discs remain permanently thinner, resulting in increased pressure and accelerated wear and tear on the facet joints.

Inevitably, there is a permanent reduction in overall height. Older people, not only appear shorter, they *are* shorter. Reliable anthropological tables give the mean height of men of 25 years of age at 5'9" (1.75m), at 60 it has reduced to 5'7" (1.70m). For women at 25, mean height is 5'4" (1.65m), reducing at 60 to 5'2" (1.57m).

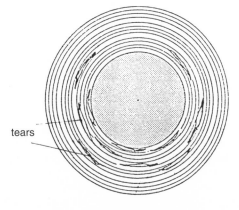

tears

Fig.33. Microscopic, fragmented tears.

THE ANNULUS

We are discussing the wearing process of discs, and we now look at the annulus. Given elastic bands of the type used in office work, you can expect them to get old, brittle and break. The elastic bands of the annulus go through exactly the same process. Although it may take many years, it is reflected by the elastic fibres developing microscopic, fragmented tears (Fig. 33).

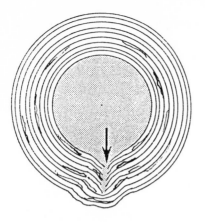

Fig.34. The "Herniated" Disc.

These tears tend to begin near the centre, which gives rise to an unequal pressure being exerted by the nucleus. The tears slowly become more extensive, until they finally merge into larger tears that fragment and weaken the structure, eventually diminishing its elastic recoil quality so essential to function (Fig 34).

At the beginning, the inherent structural strength of the annulus is great enough to compensate for this degenerate change, and the elastic bands continue to do their job of containing and directing the increases of pressure within the nucleus. However, once the process has begun, any lifting or bending which stresses the spine, can increase the number and severity of these tears over time, thus setting the stage for a possible rupture of the jelly-like material through the outer core of the annulus, producing the typical "Herniated Disc" (See Fig. 34 again).

Once the stage is set, it can happen with startling suddenness, even a simple movement, such as picking up a piece of paper or the soap in the shower, tipping the scales. How does a simple act like this trigger off such disastrous consequences? It occurs in four stages:-

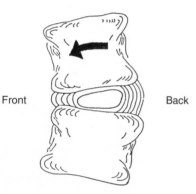

Front   Back

Fig.35. Stage 1. The trunk flexes forward.

Stage 1
As the trunk flexes, the disc is compressed at the front, but opens up at the back where there is less resistance to the build up of pressures (Fig. 35).

Stage 2
The trunk is now raised, its weight increasing the compression on the discs (Fig. 36). The pressure within the disc rises suddenly, violently driving the material in the sac backwards. The mounting pressure in the sac becomes too great for the weakened elastic bands and it bursts through, pushing and squeezing any intact fibres in front of it until it reaches the deep surface of the ligament, or backwards and sidewards

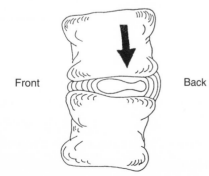

Front   Back

Fig.36. Stage 2. The trunk is raised; its weight increases the compression on the disc and drives the sac of fluid violently backwards.

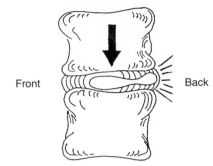

Fig.37. Stage 3. With the trunk straight the path taken by the herniating mass is closed off locking the vertebrae and the disc. The bulge remains trapped.

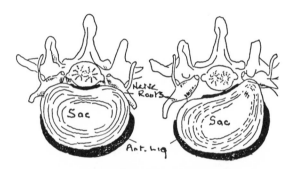

Fig.38. Compressed nerve root resulting from "Herniated" Disc.

(a) Flat Back, no lumber curve.

(b) Inability to reach below knees without pain.

Fig.39. Non-specific signs of back injury.

until it reaches a nerve root which may be lying in its path.

Stage 3

With the trunk nearly upright, the path taken by the herniating mass is closed off by the pressure of the weight of the trunk, virtually locking the vertebrae and discs, so the bulge remains trapped (Fig. 37).

Stage 4

Since it is a mechanical injury and not a pathological disease, it can temporarily regress, either spontaneously in time or with treatment. With repeated attacks, the bulge grows and protrudes more and more, generally at the edge of the ligament, which is its weakest point, or into the canal from which the nerve root emerges, irritating it. The squeezed nerve might finally be jammed against the back wall of the canal (Fig. 38), thus producing the classic "sciatica". (From Kapandji, I.A. Vol.3.)

NERVE ROOTS AND MUSCLE SPASM

An exposed nerve root is the human equivalent to a 40,000 volt uninsulated electric cable, and any irritation to it will produce excruciating pain. Instinctively, to protect the nerve root against further irritation, the muscles go into spasm, and a posture is imposed that splints that area in the position of least discomfort (Fig. 39a).

Muscle spasm is a reflex, involuntary contraction of a muscle. Any contracted muscle, whether voluntary or involuntary, will eventually fatigue as waste products build up within the muscle, producing pain and stiffness. In a voluntary contraction, this is relieved by relaxing the muscle, which allows the circulation to remove the waste products and restore the status quo, but if it is involuntary as in spasm due to an underlying injury, relaxation is impossible and the pain increases.

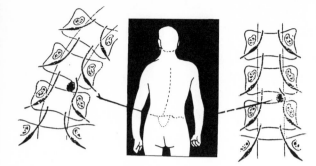

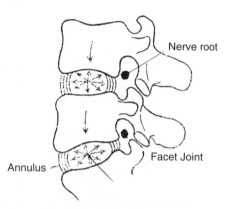

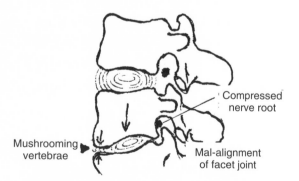

A defensive posture triggered by muscle spasm ensues, which defies any attempts to "straighten up", because it is likely to put more tension on the nerve root and increase the discomfort (Fig. 40). In an acute stage, only lying down, a position of least danger for the back, may reduce the muscle spasm and offer some relief.

It should now be more apparent why complete and permanent recovery is rare, and once a back is injured, it is three times easier to do it again. What happened is obviously not the result of a disease process, but rather a mechanical breakdown, (Figs. 41 and 42a,b) and you can be quite sure that drinking cod liver oil laced with orange juice, eating garlic, wiring your bed with copper wire, tying bits of rubber to your car, will be a total waste of time. There appears to be more cures for backs, it seems, than there are for haemorrhoids!

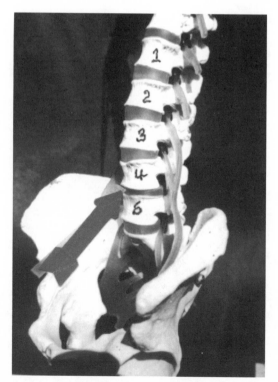

Fig.40. Muscle spasm splints the area. "Straightening up" increases tension on nerve root.

Fig.41. Normal discs with evenly distributed compression forces.

Fig.42a. With degeneration of the annulus and destruction of the nucleus, the space between the vertebrae narrows, producing pressure on the front of the bone.
The vertebrae mushrooms and there is incongruity of the facet joints, with a narrowing of the nerve root canal.

Fig.42b. The disc between vertebra 4 and 5 has prolapsed.

X-RAYS

In most cases, the diagnosis of a herniated disc can be made on the basis of the history and physical examination. Plain radiographs of the lumbo-sacral spine usually will not add any information, but nevertheless must be obtained to rule out other pathological conditions, such as a tumour or bony abnormality.

Whilst X-rays may identify the degree of degeneration in an intervertebral disc, it cannot indicate the definitive severity of symptoms. The narrowing of a disc may be barely visible in an X-ray, yet produce sufficient mal-alignment on the facet joints to cause inflammation and pain. The clinical symptoms of degeneration generally precede the X-ray picture, and the pain and discomfort will also vary with a patient's tolerance from day to day.

OTHER DIAGNOSTIC MODALITIES

The C.T. Scan. (Computerised Tomography)

Very useful for evaluating abnormalities of the lumbo-sacral spine. It creates cross sectional images of the spine at various levels, and, with reformatting, one can also obtain images in different planes. The C.T. Scan assesses not only the bony configuration, but also the soft tissue in graded shadings, so that the ligaments, nerve roots, fat and intervertebral disc protrusions can be evaluated as they relate to their bony environment.

Myelography

Myelography is the established method for evaluating nerve root compression before surgical intervention. A water soluble dye is injected which acts as a contrast dye and allows abnormalities to be more easily identified.

Electromyography

The electromyogram (EMG) determines if the nerve supply to the involved muscle is intact. An abnormal EMG can demonstrate impaired nerve transmission to a specific muscle and isolate the nerve root involved. It is not a screening tool in the evaluation of the average low back problem.

Thermography

Thermography records changes in skin temperature; areas that are "hotter" than normal are believed to represent locations of increased pain. The exact role of the thermogram in the diagnosis of low back problem is not yet clear. The prospective studies performed to date have demonstrated no diagnostic value for thermography, and at present its usefulness is in question.

Magnetic Resonance Imaging

Magnetic Resonance Imaging (MRI) is now coming into general use as a diagnostic tool. The image is obtained by an evaluation of the differences in proton density of the tissues studied. This approach is non-invasive — in contrast to Myelography. It holds great promise because of its high theoretical limits in image detail and its very low attendant risks.

Chapter 7

THE MECHANICS OF THE SPINE

We have now seen how the spine develops from infancy, and we have discussed the structure and function of the discs to establish a causal link for low back pain, or as it is sometimes called, "low back insufficiency" or "dysfunction". "Insufficiency" suggests that somehow the design of our spine is inadequate, in fact this would be quite wrong.

My admiration for the human spine knows no bounds; it is a magnificent piece of engineering, but it was simply not designed to be a crane. It is the man-made environment and our attitude to lifting that is creating this insufficiency.

The different organs of the human body have varying life expectations. For instance, your heart may show signs of wear at 55, your kidneys at 60 and your lungs, (if you don't smoke), perhaps at 90. Under normal conditions, this time frame is a function of genetic inheritance, plus environmental factors.

I will illustrate this. Supposing you have inherited a heart whose genetic time frame is say, 60 years, but environmentally, your work is not demanding, you like to keep fit, watch your weight and do all things in moderation. Under such a favourable environment, your heart may very well still be in good shape by 70, or even 80 years of age. On the other hand, if your job was physically demanding, you never exercised, but allowed yourself to get overweight and maintained an excessive life style, it is very probable your heart may not last its programmed 60 years.

This is why two people, with exactly the same job all their lives, may see one with continual back problems, whilst the other never experiences the slightest discomfort. The latter is most likely getting the benefit of a better genetic inheritance in terms of the spine. Equally by the same rationale of genetic selection, the former could be the victim of a heart attack or a stroke at 40.

Genetic research still has a long way to go , and the perennial question of where genetic inheritance ends and environment begins is largely unresolved. The effect of different environments on separated, but identical twins is interesting, but still speculative. In the absence of any underlying pathology, the current wisdom is that structural inheritance and environment must be the two factors which inter-relate to have a profound effect on early spinal degeneration. The logic is inescapable, and definitive research into this area of back physiology is long overdue.

We cannot, as yet, alter the genetic component of our spines, but we can certainly reduce the environmental stress which is such a critical factor in determining whether we are going to become a back statistic at 30, or 60. To understand this, we now look at the mechanics of the spine.

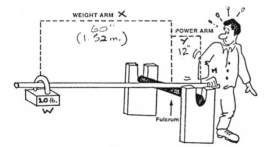

Fig.43. Lifting a cantilevered bar with a weight arm longer than the power arm means you exert a pressure greater than the weight being lifted. (in this instance by a factor of approx. 5).

THE LEVER PRINCIPLE

The spine operates as a simple Class 1 type lever. Take a 6' (1.83m) bar and a 20lb (9kg) weight, attach the weight 12" (30mm) from one end, balance the bar as shown in Fig.43, now try to lift it. You will find it very heavy indeed and will probably need two hands to do it. Why should this be so difficult? After all, its only a 20lb (9kg) weight.

With sincere apologies for this oversimplistic example shown

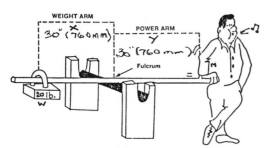

Fig.44. The lift can be made easier by moving the fulcrum nearer the weight, thus shortening the weight arm of the lever. In this example both arms of the lever are equal; there is no advantage or disadvantage, and the pressure exerted equals the weight lifted!

in Fig. 43; the facts are that in a simple lever system, the weight supported by the fulcrum (F) is the sum of the weights acting at each end of the lever bar X and Y, thus:

W = 20lbs. (9kg) W x X = M x Y

X = 60" (1.52m) 20 x 60" = M x 12" (300mm)

Y = 12" (300mm)   M = 100lbs (45.5.kg)

Total weight lifted;

M + W = 120 lbs (54.5kg)

W = Weight of object

X = Distance from the centre of gravity

Y = Distance of muscles from the centre of gravity

M = Strain developed by the muscles

However, the lift can be made easier as in Fig. 44 by moving the fulcrum nearer the weight. Thus:

W = 20lbs (9kg) W x X = M x Y

X = 30" (760mm)   20 x 30" = M x 30" (760mm)

Y = 30" (760mm)   M = 20lbs (9kg)

Total weight lifted: M x W = 40lbs (18kg)

By increasing any component of a simple lever arm, the total weight superimposed on the supporting structure can be altered.

In bending down to lift using the back, it is estimated that a person of 5'6" (1.68mm) stature is operating on a lever with a ten to one ratio of disadvantage. The practical interpretation means that, if you were to lift a 50lb (22.5kg) weight with straight legs, the stress is not 50lbs (22.5kg) on the lumbar spine, but ten times that, or 500lbs, (226.5kg) and is a significantly heavier weight.

The example of this mechanical principle presented in the human spine will be immediately appreciated in Figs. 45 &

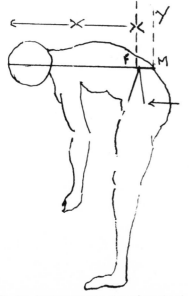

Fig.45. Analogous equation of mechanical forces on the human spine.

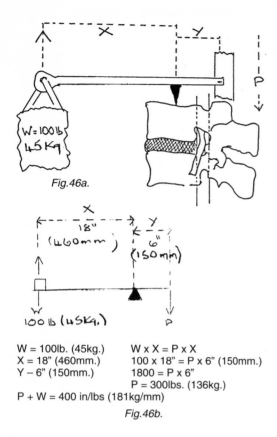

Fig. 46a.

W = 100lb. (45kg.)   W x X = P x X
X = 18" (460mm.)   100 x 18" = P x 6" (150mm.)
Y – 6" (150mm.)   1800 = P x 6"
                     P = 300lbs. (136kg.)
P + W = 400 in/lbs (181kg/mm)

Fig.46b.

46a and b. (From Prof. E. R. Tichauer)

Research on the maximum tolerances for human discs vary between 340lbs (154kg) and 1760lbs (798kg). (Kapandji). This suggests that perhaps a repetitive lift of 150lbs (68kg) producing 1500lbs (680kg) (15 x 10) pressure on the lumbar discs could well be within acceptable limits.

Of course, such loads would be impossible for a normal average person, and the reasons the numbers mentioned do not appear to make sense is **the weight of the trunk.** With the male trunk weighing approximately 100lbs (45kg), the leverage is such that, merely the act of tying your shoelaces, if carried out with straight legs using the spine to straighten up, imposes a pressure on the lumbar discs of over 1,000lbs (453.5kg) and adds up to a completely different stress factor. We must also include ten times the weight held in the arms.

Nevertheless, allowing for an upper destructive limit for the disc of 1,760lbs (798kg), a 10 to 1 lever ratio, and a trunk factor of 1,000lbs (453.5kg), we should presumably be able to cope with repetitive loads of 76lbs (34.5kg), except that 1,760lbs (798kg) upper stress limit is only an approximate maximum for a young, healthy adult of about 20 years of age; at 30, the normal degenerative change will have reduced the upper limit to approximately 1,500lbs (680.5kg); by 40, it will be down to 1,250lbs (567kg); at 50, it will be under 1,000lbs (453.5kg), and at my age, it is probably about 2lb (1kg) maximum.

It is, therefore, not surprising that you bend to lift apparently nothing heavier than a piece of paper off the floor or the soap in the shower, and you set in motion an acute back condition. Unfortunately, you did not pick up a piece of paper or the soap in the shower;the fact is, you picked up the weight of your trunk, approx. 1,000lbs (543.5kg) on a spine that has been steadily deteriorating since you were 20 years old. You have been virtually a back injury waiting to happen.

Dr. I. A. Kapandji, former head of the surgical clinic of The Hospital of Paris, in his excellent work the "Physiology of Joints", states that "lifting a 10lbs (4.5kg) weight with bent knees puts a strain on the spine of about 141kg (310lbs). Lifting the same weight with straight knees changes it to 256kg (563lbs). The forces generated can often range from 282kg (620lbs) to 760kg (1,672lbs), and even up to 1,200kg (2,640lbs). This is more than any force required to disrupt the discs, which is estimated as 850kg (1,760lbs) in the young and 450kg (990lbs) in the aged." The last category means that by the age of 55 or over, the spine is probably operating on its maximum loading capacity at all times by virtue of the weight of the trunk alone.

It has been for this reason that the almost universally recognised repetitive lift limit has been set at 40lbs (18kg) for adult males and 28lbs (13kg) for adult females, floor to knuckle height. A repetitive lift being more than once every 2 minutes. (From S. Snook. "The Design of Manual Handling Tasks" Ergonomic Society Lecture 1978.)

Dr E. R. Tichauer, Project Director, New York University Medical Center, in his brilliant, original monograph on the biomechanics of lifting, presents his research to show that a 30lbs (13.5kg) weight lifted with straight legs imposed a strain of 3,190lbs (1,477kg) on the lumbar discs (Fig.47a).

The list goes on. Dr A. Nachemson, of Sweden, one of the world's leading orthopaedic surgeons on low back injury, states that the pressure on the L 3 disc lifting 20kg (44lbs) with a straight back and knees bent is 210kg (463lbs), without the weight of the trunk; lifting the same weight with a bent back and knees straight is 340kg (749lbs). The same weight is almost doubled by lifting with the back instead of the legs.

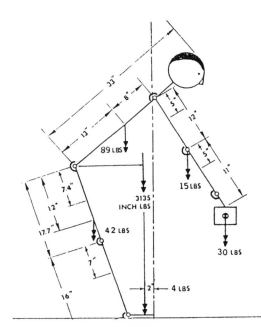

Fig.47a. A 30lb. (13.5kg) lift with straight legs imposes a strain of 3,190lbs. (1,447kg.) on the lumbar spine. (From, Tichauer, E.R. Occ.Biomechanics.)

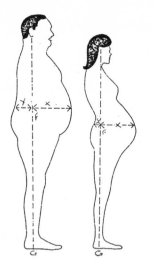

Fig.47b. Pregnancy and obesity load the spine by increasing the weight arm of the lever.

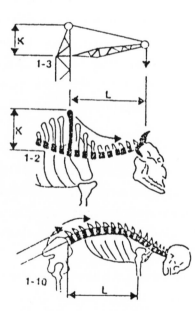

Fig.48. Of all creatures it is only man that must contend with such poor adaption. Ratios of power arm to weight arm, ;- Tower crane - 1 to 3, Buffalo - 1 to 2. Man - 1 to 10.

The effects of this lever principle is again well illustrated in the very common pre-natal or post-natal back pain. The foetus and the water represents a weight of perhaps 15lbs (6.8kg) in the front of the spine of a pregnant mother, but the loading on the lumbar spine represented by the longer weight arm could be nearer 115lbs (68kg) (Fig.47b). Consistent stress of this nature every day for the last few weeks of pregnancy, particularly if early degeneration is present, would be quite enough to precipitate a chronic low back condition.

In the same category are obese people, also loading their spines in very much the same way as pregnant women. Indeed, the principles are identical (Fig. 47b). Obesity can almost be viewed as a state of permanent pregnancy, with not only the same potential mechanical problems, but with the added handicap of flabby abdominal muscles as well. Controlling back pain may be said to begin by keeping your weight down.

Of all creatures, it is only man who must contend with such poor adaptation (Fig. 48). An animal on all fours is a bridge-like structure, on which it only needs to lift its head and neck, which is why most animals do not get degenerated discs in the way man does.

The simplicity with which the leverage of the spine can be changed to reduce the strain, again raises the question of whether the grand design is all it should be. The answer would have to be an unequivical "yes". The mechanics of the spine are a triumph of speed at the expense of strength. Civilisation owes very little of its development to strength. Were strength to be man's dominant feature, we would have gone the way of the dinosaurs a long time ago. It was speed, our ability to get out of danger in a hurry that brought us safely along the evolutionary road.

A small movement at the fulcrum of the lumbar region results in a very large, fast arc of movement for the whole trunk,

Fig.49. That 3 pound fish could feel like a whale; its all a question of levers.

particularly the head. Self preservation began here; it was vital to our survival.

A fishing rod (Fig 49) or holding a sledge hammer at the end of the handle, are similar types of levers, which provide practical examples of the advantages of speed and range of movement for the sacrifice of strength.

Nevertheless, despite the research, despite the statistical attention it receives, despite the publicity, our efforts at significantly reducing this problem over the last 50 years has only been marginally successful.

There is nothing wrong with the structure or the physiology of the spine. What is wrong is how we are using it in an environment that continues to disregard our limitations. It was never intended to be a mobile crane; rather, it was designed to protect the spinal cord, support the skeleton and its contents, and provide us with movement, all of which it does admirably. But instead of climbing, running, hunting and fishing, we have become a species of spectators, spending as much time sitting, driving, eating and watching T.V. as we do working.

It is only lately that we have realised that exercise and keeping fit is not some adolescent fad but necessary to the human condition. It is also the prerequisite for protecting the spine from environmental stress, but this begins with knowing what is the correct and safe way to bend and lift. Early degeneration is part of the price we are paying for this omission.

What we have been discussing is the disabling back injury, resulting from no apparent cause or triggered by an action such as lifting or bending. There are, of course, other reasons for acute back pain. Many diseases affect the spine, such as Ankylosing Spondylitis, Cancer, Tuberculosis of the spine, or

Osteoporosis to name a few, but these only make up a relatively small proportion of the causes of back pain compared to degenerative conditions. Our area of concern here is the 75% of people who bend down to pick up nothing heavier than their handkerchief and become a back statistic, or the worker who walks into his plant in the morning feeling great, and by midday with no known cause is in agony.

A back injury can certainly be of muscular origin. Muscles can be strained or torn anywhere, but the massive nature of the back muscles makes it unusual. Unfortunately, this diagnosis as the reason for back pain is used far more often than is justified. How does one know? The clinical picture is very similar – pain, muscle spasm and limitation of movement. Nevertheless, there are positive diagnostic procedures to establish the difference between a degenerative back and a muscle strain, although perhaps not immediately. Muscle strains or tears heal. An athlete will tear a muscle and be breaking the mile record a month later – as, in fact, many runners, including New Zealand's John Walker, has proved. It is when a back injury returns again and again for no apparent reason and no supporting causology, that a degenerative condition must be suspected and a long term rehabilitative regime considered.

Chapter 8
CORRECT BENDING AND LIFTING

THE RESEARCH MAZE

As an Ergonomist, specialising in Cumlative Trauma Disorders, I have become increasingly concerned with the many solutions offered for the back injury and the difficulties associated with those solutions. For instance, we now know there is a correlation between the horizontal location of a load, the vertical location, the vertical distance displayed by the load, and the lifting frequency to the stress experienced by the spine.

There are biomechanical lifting models, and then, dynamic biomechanical lifting models. There are also metabolic lifting models and cardio-vascular lifting models, all apparently show the way to structure safe lifting techniques.

The optimum size for a box has been researched, and the best position of its handles has been located. We now also know the maximum permissible safe loads for lifting, pushing, pulling, or simply holding.

While all this research activity over the last decade has been painstaking and highly commendable, it has not made any noticable difference to the frequency and severity of the back injuries in industry, nor has it reduced the back pain of a long suffering general public.

What is not being addressed is that a very high percentage of the so-called back injuries occur lifting nothing heavier than a piece of paper or a handkerchief off the floor.

Generally speaking, we can summarise the pathology of spinal degeneration as a lowered structural resistance in the disc, leading to the formation of fissures which results in a loss of fluid and, therefore, narrowing of the discs. This produces increased pressure on the joint surfaces, particularly in facet joints and bony areas of the spine, thus initiating and then accelerating a wear and tear cycle.

Structural resistance is a factor of genetic inheritance and environmental stress. Environmental stress will be largely determined by what you lift, how you lift, and the ergonomics of the work environment, e.g. frequency of lift, weight, distance carried, etc.

There is nothing that can be done at present to reverse any genetic causology for back pain. But the environmental causology leads to two points of view, and here I quote the eminent back physiologist, John R. Brown: "Either Management and educational organisations have been ineffective in preventing back injuries by teaching people to lift safely, or the so-called safe lifting techniques are not adequate for people's daily actions in their home or work environment, or both".

In the past, many lifting techniques for preventing back injury have been advocated with titles such as "Kinetic" or "Dynamic" or "Mechanical", etc. All are based on the concept that, since the spine functions as a lever with a mechanical disadvantage of ten to one, if you can change the equation by keeping your back straight (vertical) when you lift, all will be well. This produced a crop of "experts" and techniques, which were theoretically correct and had an interesting potential to minimise injury, but they were never popular or effective because they relied on a set of instructions, which for the average person was difficult to do and remember. Lifting for most people is a simple action which they prefer to carry out almost on a subconscious level, and with a minimum of thought or effort; bending down is not exactly an intellectual exercise!

A few years ago, I conducted an experiment at a pharmaceutical warehouse in Britain, one of the largest of its kind in the world. I was studying storemen packers with back problems. It was to be a comprehensive study of the methods people use in lifting. It produced some interesting facts!

One of the most significant was that the storemen carried out some 1,500 observed lifts, and on only 127 occasions did any worker bend his or her knees, a mere 8.4% of the total. Also, I was unable to record any single occasion where a storeman lifted an object with his back "straight" (vertical), despite the fact that they had earlier identified the "straight back method" as the correct lifting technique from a chart showing various lifting positions.

Lifting is often done in confined spaces with bulky loads, not only varying in size and shape, but paced to a degree that has a direct relationship on performance. The way it is done will surely be a matter of stature, strength, and the dimensions and capacity of the container being loaded, regardless of whether it is a pallet, a freight container, or a kitchen cupboard.

With such work conditions and settings, it is not surprising that the impact of instruction on "lifting" is ineffective in changing performance. It succeeds only in producing a credibility gap in its practical application, and very quickly has people returning to their old, expedient, but unsafe, patterns of bending and lifting; generally, this means with straight legs, using their lower back like a crane. (Fig. 50)

WRONG

Fig.50.

KINETIC SIX POINT LIFTING

Unfortunately, practical back injury prevention training has never been very successful, because for decades it has been dominated by a technique known as "Kinetic six point lifting", which with variations goes like this:-

1. Feet astride
2. One foot in front of the other to form a pyramid shape.
3. The front foot turned in the direction you intend to go to avoid twisting.
4. Get a good grip.
5. Bend your knees.
6. Keep your back straight (vertical).
   Now Lift!

This sounds quite reasonable in the light of our previous chapters, and you may wonder what's wrong with it? The only thing wrong with it is that it cannot be done. Lifting with a straight back is awkward and difficult, because it places the centre of gravity for the trunk so far back, that the lifter is unstable and in danger of falling over backwards. You are being asked to do a "tango" with your feet whilst remembering six specific instructions. It just doesn't work because it is unnatural and uncomfortable, and the evidence is overwhelming for those who care to look for it.

I believe this pattern can be changed only if two basic considerations are met. The first is the acceptance of a simple practical technique for safe lifting that requires no feat of memory and is possible in almost any situation, and the second is to appreciate the physical hazards associated with bending and lifting, and to utilise practical ergonomic principles to design them out of the work environment.

RIGHT

Fig.51. – Correct Lifting
The simplicity of "BEND YOUR KNEES"

Fig.52. Position the action as best suits you, but use your thighs to make the lift.

CORRECT LIFTING MADE SIMPLE

Basic correct bending and lifting can be defined as simply using yours legs to make the lift and not your back. A natural lift, has two elements:-

1. Stand as close to the weight as you can with the knees bent and the back in a comfortable position. This is not necessarily straight, oblique or curved. The size and shape of the object itself will limit the degree of knee bend and the angle of the spine, although it is not advisable to squat right down to near floor level (Fig. 51).

2. Now lift by straightening the knees to the upright position. If this is not possible because the object is some distance away, carry out element No. 1. and use a combined effort by the arms and shoulder to pull the object close to the body. As this occurs, there is straightening of the legs, resulting in a full standing position. The movement occurs simultaneously and results in a smooth co-ordinated action.

The complete naturalness of this lift is self evident.. That is to say, you position the action as best suits you, offering the least amount of strain. Only one element requires emphasis, this is; **"BEND YOUR KNEES AND LIFT WITH YOUR LEGS"**. Once learned and adopted, the spine will unconsciously assume an angle that is comfortable and natural. This will be a synthesis of body dimensions, the weight, the size of the load, and the space available for the lift (Fig. 52).

The thighs contain the largest and most powerful muscle groups in the body. Compared with the spine, there is no vulnerable sacs of fluid, no outer rings of elastic bands, no nerve roots, just a shaft of bone (the femur), surrounded by a mass of muscle (quadriceps and hamstrings). Degeneration is not a factor, and strain of these muscles is not common, even among weightlifters.

Fig.53. Natural Bending

I am suggesting that the focus for safe lifting and back injury protection is in the wrong place. It is time we started emphasising the legs as the most important element in back injury protection, instead of being mesmerised by the angle of the spine which, under normal circumstances, will find its own position anyway. "BEND YOUR KNEES" should become the prime target for back safety promotion on lifting or bending, with the other components like the position of the feet or whether the back is straight or curved etc., relegated to a minor role in what ought to be a natural movement.

If you have any doubt that this is the way nature intended us to lift, you have only to observe infants bending at play to be convinced. You will rarely find them bending down without squatting on their haunches. They do this repetitively, all day, apparently without fatigue. Adults have been known to get tired simply watching them! (Fig. 53).

PELVIC TILTING

Even modifications like "pelvic tilting" prior to the lift, should not be encouraged as it detracts from the prime objective, which is to emphasise using the legs to make the lift. Pelvic Tilting is another of these good theories that, for general use, defies practical interpretation, particularly in a factory setting.

Fig.54. Pelvic Tilting.

Derived from weight training techniques, stabilising of the lumbar spine was seen as the key factor in preventing back strain in competition weightlifting, and there is no doubt that it will (Fig. 54). However, it is one thing for an inspired dedicated weightlifter to learn and remember if he wishes to be a champion, and quite another for an industrial worker repetitively lifting all day at a paced rate.

Quite apart from that, it is a movement that demands a great deal of co-ordinated muscular effort. To be effective, it has to be learned and maintained with every lift until it is a stereotype pattern. The reality is that, in an industrial setting, any modification of an existing work practice must be easier that what was done previously, or it will never be adopted except by undesirable coercion. "Bend Your Knees" to lift is successful precisely because it is considerably easier than the untrained stereotype lifting we see everywhere today.

Unfortunately, what is extremely frustrating is, despite the fact that "Kinetic" straight back, or "Pelvic Tilt" lifting has never caught on because of its structured approach, a reluctance to change training dogma has resulted in operators being subjected to a great deal of frustrating communication, compounded by posters showing starch coated, smiling supervisors lifting with a rigidly straight back. This, of course, merely looks like a supervisor about to make an indecent noise, and is only good for a laugh in the cafeteria. The answer all too often is generally to feign interest and ignore advice which they find difficult anyway, and to delegate safe lifting propaganda as being another of the trials of the job.

Fig.55. Lifting using only the hip joints, the short cut to the floor and a back injury.

LIFT IN THE EASIEST WAY NOT THE SIMPLEST WAY!

Despite what is known about the dangers of indiscriminate lifting, it is human nature to gravitate into doing boring activities in the simplest possible manner. The simplest way of bending is moving towards the floor with straight legs, where only one joint, the hip joint, is involved (Fig. 55); it is, in effect, a short cut to the floor. The easiest way is to bend the knees, but that means two joints, the hip and knee joints, and although it demands slightly more co-ordination, it is much easier and is just as fast.

51

I can hear the chorus of "experts" immediately saying that the energy expenditure must be greater on a two joint lift than a one joint lift, and therefore the superiority of "Bend Your Knees" is questionable. The answer to this is to point out that the criteria for injury prevention is not necessarily a function of energy expenditure; the easiest route down a scaffold might be to slide down or jump!

However, I quote again from the report submitted to the Labour Safety Council of Ontario, Canada in 1974 by Dr. J. R. Brown, Professor of Environmental Health, Faculty of Medicine, University of Toronto, and certainly the most significant pioneer of practical back injury prevention this century, who researched all the current lifting techniques and concluded: "We experimented with many different techniques of lifting, but there was no significant difference in energy expenditure between any of them".

There are also the people who have difficulties for every solution, and I hear them saying: "What about the wear and tear on the knees?" True, some people have knee problems that makes bending difficult, but it is still preferable to using the back. Painful knees can be supported by a bandage or rested by sitting. The persistent functional disability and pain of an acute back offers no relief, even in bed! However, if this is a genuine reason for not bending the knees, the solution lies in an ergonomic redesign of the operation itself.

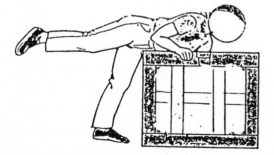

Fig.56. The Golfer's Lift.

LIFTING OPTIONS

In essence, I am saying the weight of your trunk is the critical factor. Whatever the reason, do not use your back for lifting if you can avoid it. How do you do that? It's easy. For instance, you can lean on something with one hand whilst you bend and pick it up with the other (Fig. 56). Use the wall if necessary to lean on. If there is nothing in the immediate

Fig.57. If there is nothing to lean on and you only need one hand, use your knee to support the weight of your trunk.

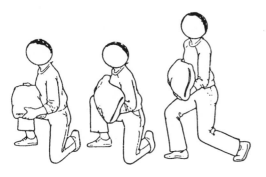

Fig.58. Push off the rear leg.

vicinity for support, kneel on one knee and use your free hand to push yourself up (Fig. 57), otherwise kick the object to where there is a good support. It will still be there long after you are a back statistic. On rare occasions when the sheer weight may make this impossible, carry out the lift on a single bent knee, using both hands to hold the object, then push off the rear leg into a standing position (Fig. 58).

LIFTING LIMITS

What is the maximum weight a person can be expected to lift safely? This is a controversial question because lifting ability depends on so many variables age, fitness, stature. How good are your abdominal and thigh muscles? What kind of a lift is it, e.g. occasional or repetitive? Are you lifting from the floor or from a table to a higher shelf? How far are you positioned from the weight, etc. etc? All these factors influence maximum lifting potential.

Valiant research efforts have been made, but there is considerable disagreement among the investigators about the maximum acceptable weight of a lift.
1. The recommendations for the 50th percentile male lifting from the floor range from 24kg (53 lbs) (Snook, Irvine and Bass, 1970) to 86kg (189 lbs) (Emanual, Chaffee and Wing, 1956).
2. There are large differences in the lifting capabilities of the male populations. The lifting capability of the weak male may be as low as 45% that of the strong male (Snook 1978).
3. The maximum weight acceptable to the 50th percentile female is to the order of 60% to 70% of the maximum weight acceptable to the 50th percentile male. (Snook 1978; Ayoub et al 1978; Snook and Cirriello 1974), whilst values as low as 40% are recommended by Grandjean 1969 and The International Labour Office, I.L.O. 1965) (J. Human Factors, Aug. 1980 P.478)

The best empirical recommendation I can give is a limit of one quarter of your bodyweight for repetitive lifting and one third the bodyweight for occasional lifting in an individual of average physical condition and who is not obese. Above this, you are entering a hazardous lifting zone and one that calls for extreme caution. To be more specific, I place the upper limit for an occasional lift (8 per hour) at approximately 60 lbs (27kg) for males, and 35 lbs (16kg) for females. For repetitive lifting (more than once every two mins.) 41 lbs (18kg) for males and 24 lbs (11kg) for females. Of course, any lift should be carried out with bent knees. (For comprehensive information on maximum lifting limits, read "The Design of Manual Handling Tasks" by Stover H. Snook. J. of Erg. Vol. 21 No. 12. P. 963-985).

The Regulations, Guidelines or Codes of Practice put out by various Government agencies to limit unreasonable manual lifting or carrying are impossible to implement. Strict adherence would virtually bring industry to a halt overnight. Obviously the Guidelines or Codes of Practice must be interpreted liberally, almost on a job by job basis. In today's work environment, operators especially if they are unskilled, will be expected, if needs be, to lift weights in excess of the established guidlines.

Even the legislation posed by equal opportunity is fraught with problems; loads cannot be designated male or female, its not the way industry works! Either the loads lifted must be reduced to female physiological limits, which would be a productive disaster for many industries, or the loads are within male limitations and may present a hazard for females. Regretfully, people do not know their physiological limits until it is too late.

The only sensible way of dealing with the problem is to require that appropriate training should be given to everybody who has to do any form of lifting as part of their work, and that ergonomic principles related to the design of materials handling tasks should be introduced wherever it is practical and economic to do so.

Chapter 12 discusses this more fully.

Chapter 9
AWARENESS V. PERFORMANCE

The devastating Polio epidemics of the late 1940's and early 1950's with graphic pictures of "iron lung" victims, provoked Governments and its scientific communities to give priority to research on the disease, and the Salk vaccine arrived. As a result, there is no necessity today to encourage populations to accept a pleasant tasting drink to prevent Polio; its so easy! Yet back injuries, which produces a far greater incidence of chronic functional disability within a population and could be just as easily prevented, goes on unabated.

Unfortunately, awareness does not necessarily influence performance, as is evident all around us. People still smoke, take drugs, drink and drive, and continue to have serious accidents in sight of dire warning posters, with apparent indifference to the message. A driver caught doing 60 miles per hour in a built up area is unlikely to be doing it because he cannot remember the speed limit. A test given to all drivers to see how much of the Highway Code they can remember would be very poorly correlated with the number of traffic offences.

Much research on this has been done. In 1956, Eunice Belbin, formerly of the Psychological Laboratory, University of Cambridge, England (1956), set up a series of experiments using Road Safety Posters to investigate why some subjects could recall the information but did not use it, while others who could not recall the information, nevertheless did use it. Belbin found there was no positive relationship between the effects of propaganda, as shown by tests of recall and recognition on the one hand, and behaviour on the roads on the other.

S. Laner and R. G. Sell in 1960 conducted an experiment for the Operational Research Department of the British Iron and Steel Research Association, to persuade workers to hook crane slings more safely, using safety posters. In 18 locations, it was found that recall was an unreliable guide to the effect posters had on actual behaviour, but rather their effectiveness was due in part to their acting as perpetual reminders for safe practices.

Nevertheless, the analogy between safety awareness campaigns and commercial advertising continues. The argument is that such vast sums of money would not be spent if the campaigns were not successful; however, this is based on a false premise. Advertising is beamed at people who already have a desire to buy the article advertised. Injury prevention on the other hand does not have this inherent sales appeal; to achieve it, people must invest time and effort in observing safe working principles and techniques.

Reducing back injuries in the general population or industry will always depend on overcoming this psychological barrier between awareness and performance, and quantitative research in this area should be a priority, rather than some of the predictable hypothesis, which appears to attract so many good scientists. For instance I believe it is not really necessary to prove that, after five days without sleep, you feel tired.

THE NEW ZEALAND EXPERIMENT

In December 1986, The New Zealand Accident Compensation Corporation, faced with mounting back injury statistics and the usual philosophic resignation that pervades back pain, decided to mount a bold experiment in an attempt to change people's apparent indifference to safe lifting techniques, and the way they thought about their backs.

It would use the media not for a conventional advertising campaign, but to mount a nationwide television programme aimed at increasing awareness of the importance of back care. It would introduce the whole population, particularly school-children, to better bending and lifting habits, without making them apprehensive about these activities, and it would motivate public acceptance towards a sense of personal responsibility for back injury prevention.

It first determined what was the most important element in a safe lifting message. It then simplified this message, so that it could be utilised as an easily remembered catchy slogan. The slogan selected was "Bend Your Knees, Your Back is Not a Crane" (From L. Ring, unpublished research thesis, Loughborough University).
It then introduced the television viewing public to some basic ergonomic concepts about back hazards in industrial and domestic work environments, and how to prevent them.

Finally, a professional market research study was authorised to measure the incidence and awareness of back problems among persons aged 18 to 30, to find out how this population behaved when required to bend and lift before and after the programme. The purpose of this market research study was to obtain a benchmark, against which the results of subsequent studies could be measured.

The first stage consisted of interviews of 1,000 randomly selected subjects. The second stage in which I was involved was a series of one minute advertisements shown at peak viewing periods, in which I strongly advised people to bend their knees whenever they go towards the floor, regardless of whether it was to lift objects or put them down, and promoted some simple exercises.

The advertisements ran for about three months and, at the end of this period, a documentary was produced and shown, titled, "The Bad Back Video", with myself as narrator explaining in simple terms the structure and mechanism of the spine, the physiology of wear and tear, and why the back is not a crane, re-emphasising "Bend Your Knees".

The logic, simplicity and urgency of the message stimulated radio talkback shows and live TV interviews, who used "Bend Your Knees" as a theme for public discussion. Even the National TV current affairs comedy team presented a skit on the slogan. This was more than was hoped for, and added an unexpected bonus and interest to the campaign.

The final phase following this period was again interviewing the original 1,000 subjects to determine whether any of the old attitudes towards back injury awareness and performance had changed. The most significant findings of these were:

1.   On the major causes of back injuries, such as lifting, bending, lack of exercise, strains or falls, etc, lifting was regarded by more than half (54%) as a major back injury cause, and those who viewed back injuries most seriously now named bending as the major cause.

2.   On the awareness of promotional material on back problems and lifting, of the 97 people in 100 who recalled advertising, promotion or information, 92 said they had seen it on television. The corresponding figure in 1985 was only 22 of the 79 who recalled.

3. On the effect of such material in changing or modifying lifting behaviour, 9 respondents in 10 (88%) claimed that seeing or hearing promotional material had effected the way in which they treated their backs, and 28% to 49% were more specific in stating that they had now changed the way in which they lifted objects or bent down.

An unexpected reward for the campaign was that the national

television network was so impressed with the programme's objectives, that they donated a great deal of air time to free advertising as a public service.

Doctors, pre-natal and post-natal exercise clinics, schools and industry continue, even now, after 6 years to use the videofilm "The Bad Back Video" as a training aid. Other material and supporting posters that complemented the campaign are still being used some 3-4 years after the programme has finished, and there has been a keen international interest in the advertisements and the documentary.

I am not suggesting that such a campaign is the complete answer for back injury prevention. Obviously, there are other equally important elements, like ergonomics, good accident investigation, management attitudes and so on, but I commend this as a first time novel approach to the problem by a small country, whose accident prevention agency had the courage and initiative to act decisively on a national level.

The experiment is not presented as some statistically validated research study. A television campaign and a market research audit is not exactly quantitative research procedure. Now, long after the campaign has concluded, the slogan, "Bend Your Knees, your back is not a crane", has become a catchphrase in New Zealand that can be found handwritten on cartoons, containers and cranes, and is used everywhere to caution or admonish people bending badly.

I believe the programme was successful, because what was being asked of the population did not involve a sacrifice, like giving up smoking, or drinking. Equally, it was not a feat of memory, like the six point lifting technique. It was essentially an appeal, so succinct and reasonable that anything more would have appeared unnecessary, and anything less would have been futile.

Programmes of this type often do not live up to expectations, because invariably they finish too abruptly or do not plan for long term reinforcement. Also, if one of the objectives is to change stereotype performance, then surely the most important group to concentrate on must be our schoolchildren from intermediate level onwards. The importance of this group should never be underestimated in any campaign aimed at the long term control of back injuries.

Training schoolchildren in correct lifting techniques and creating the right habit patterns is not only far easier than when they are adults, but it can be given practical interpretation in the gymnasium. It will also provide a receptive base from which the message can be reinforced when they become apprentices or go on to University. Only then, might industry be able to avoid the present high frequency, and the frustrating, uphill task of constant retraining, plus the cost associated with back injuries and its prevention.

Awareness and performance in the prevention of back injury remains a contentious area of research, because like pain itself, it is difficult to measure and evaluate. However, the unusual nature and success of the New Zealand experience suggests that the use of the media to increase awareness via T.V. advertisements and videofilms, might influence the strength of a training message to the degree that the warning becomes more acceptable, and the performance relating to it more consistent and sustained.

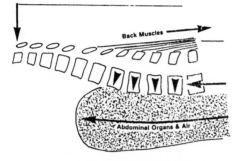

Fig.59. Intra-Abdominal Pressure.
When you lift, the back muscles attached to the spine are working very strongly; however the front of the vertebrae resting on abdominal organs is unsupported, creating a tendency to push the vertebrae into the abdominal cavity.

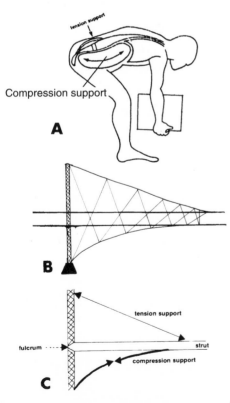

Fig.60. The Spine as a cantilevered bridge.

Chapter 10

"DOES EXERCISE MAKE ANY DIFFERENCE?"

If it were not for an ingenious piece of human engineering, everybody in the world would have a back problem by the age of 20. The abdominal cavity is almost a sealed container holding the stomach, intestines, colon, kidneys, liver, bladder, spleen and pancreas. It also contains a certain amount of air and, therefore, there is always an "air pressure" in the abdominal cavity.

Look at diagram Fig. 59 to the left of this paragraph and notice that when you bend, your lumbar vertebrae lies on the abdominal organs and is virtually unsupported. Under normal circumstances, on lifting the trunk from a forward bending position there is a tendency to push the spine downwards into the abdominal cavity. This could result in increased tension in the muscles and discs of the lumbar area in lifting and might also subject the abdominal organs to a great deal of pressure; fortunately, the tendency is more apparent than real.

On bending, the air is compressed, raising its pressure to create a firm base of support underneath the lumbar spine, making it possible for the back muscles to exert a positive pull. The effect is similar to the engineering of a cantilevered bridge, with the back muscles providing the tension support holding the bridge up, and the intra-abdominal pressure providing the compression support that keeps the bridge from collapsing (Fig. 60a,b,c).

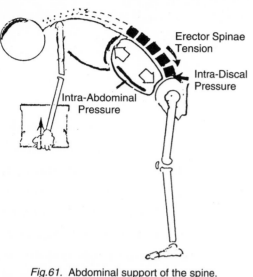

Erector Spinae Tension

Intra-Discal Pressure

Intra-Abdominal Pressure

Fig.61. Abdominal support of the spine. The intra-abdominal pressures created during lifting decrease the pressure exerted by stress forces on the disc. This substantiates the need for strong abdominal muscles to ensure a strong back.

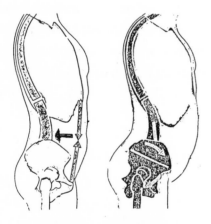

Fig.62. Sagging abdominal muscles will not support anything.

It is estimated that good intra-abdominal pressure reduces the strain on the discs in lifting by as much as 40%. However, good intra-abdominal pressure depends entirely on good abdominal muscles. (Fig. 61)

Weak abdominal muscles will not support anything. Let us view the spine once again as the mast of a ship; this time, with the back muscles as one guy rope and the abdominal muscles as the other guy rope. If the guy rope in front is slack and sagging, the mast is in danger of collapsing and will certainly do so under stress. (Fig. 61)

There are, therefore, two large muscle groups responsible for the integrity of the spine, the back muscles and the abdominal muscles. Whilst the back muscles do not readily lose condition, you do not see people with fat backs, because we use the back muscles all day simply to maintain erect posture even when sitting; the abdominal muscles do not come in for this continuous built-in exercise. We sit for most of our daily activities, from work to recreation, with abdominal muscles relaxed, and getting weaker. Added to that, is the fact that with approaching middle age, putting on fat around the abdomen is a secondary male sex characteristic compounding the problem. (Fig. 62)

I believe the abdominal muscles are the most important group in the prevention of a back injury. For effective back injury control, firstly, bend your knees to lift, but secondly, keep your abdominal muscles in good shape.

So important is the relationship between abdominal muscle strength and back injuries, that, by choice, it has become a focus for pre-employment testing for many large U.S. corporations rather than X-rays which have proved unreliable for determining potential back problems.

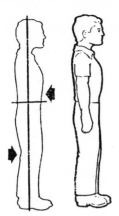

Fig.63. Pelvic Tilting.

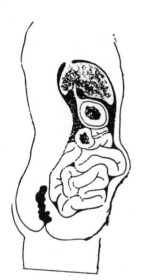

Fig.64. Weak abdominal wall and Hernia.

An excellent exercise for maintaining this intra-abdominal pressure is pelvic tilting, which is carried out as follows:-

1.   Stand with feet comfortably apart,
2.   Bend knees slightly
3.   Tuck in the stomach,
4.   Tighten buttock muscles,
5.   Tilt the pelvic backwards.

The action is similar to a Tahitian hula, but only in the forward and backward direction. It is best done slowly in both the standing and lying position (Fig. 63). Try doing it whenever you can, such as standing at a bench or waiting in line for something. Obviously, discretion must be exercised or you might get arrested! It is important to see in perspective that I am not suggesting pelvic tilting as a pre-lift manoeuvre, for reasons already stated in Chapter 8, but simply as a good abdominal exercise.

It is easy to see why back injuries and a hernia, which is only a tear in the muscle wall, are two sides of the same coin. An injured back forced to lift, yet unable to cope, will result in higher intra-abdominal pressures that may precipitate a hernia. Conversely, an existing hernia may, because of a weak abdominal wall, force back muscles to work harder to overcome the reduction in intra-abdominal pressure, thus precipitating or increasing the potential for a back injury (Fig. 64).

ARE WEIGHTLIFTING BELTS JUSTIFIED?

A relatively new request from materials handlers is for weight-lifting belts. This fad gained popularity several years ago among weight lifters, who realised that increasing intra-abdominal pressure might give them a physiological edge over their opposition. With time, other weightlifters anxious not to lose any small physiological or psychological advantage, also began to use such belts, and today, similar to wrist supports, it has become almost a uniform appendage to weightlifting gear.

Qualified research into all sorts of lifting has shown that people hold their breath during exertion, and it is the effects of this that appears to increase intra-abdominal pressure and reduce the lumbar compressive loads, whether they are wearing belts or not. The research also demonstrated that there was no advantage to be gained by weightlifters performing a dead lift or squat lifts by wearing belts. The conclusions reached were that the muscle activity (erector spinae) and the intra-abdominal pressure results of the study during short duration lifting tasks made it difficult to justify the prescription of abdominal belts to workers. (McGill, S.M. et al. Dept. of Kinesiology, University of Waterloo, Ontario. 1990).

Nevertheless, the request for such belts from workers, or working weightlifters, is becoming more demanding and is usually coincidental to allowing weight trainers to address industrial workers on the care of the back and safe lifting.

I have shown how intra-abdominal pressure is influenced by the tone of the abdominal muscles, and the way it affects the spine in lifting, but what must be equally realised is that a belt is no substitute for the abdominal muscles. The integrity of a muscle is very dependent on its continual use, and it responds quickly to any kind of support by an immediate reduction in tone and fitness. This is evident when a limb has been immobilised in plaster for a period.

The main advantage of an abdominal belt for lifters is that, if it fits correctly and is tight enough and wide enough to cover the abdominal cavity (an essential prerequisite), it may indeed marginally assist the lifter, but if it fulfilled this criteria, it would also be so tight as to impede free movement of the trunk. Indeed, this is the rationale for the surgical corset. (Fig. 65)

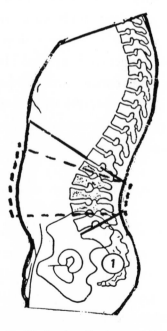

Fig.65. A belt to be affective would have to be as wide as the abdominal wall. In an all day task it would frustrate free trunk movement. Obviously it is not a substitute for the abdominal muscles.

For a weightlifter with good abdominals in the first instance and occupied with a two hour competition or a workout, its use will not cause any harmful effects that are not offset by a few extra pounds on his weightlifting total, but he would be well advised not to wear it for routine training if he wants to maintain optimum abdominal muscle strength (Harman et al 1989). However, for an industrial worker to wear it all day, creates the danger of diminishing abdominal tone to the degree that, when it is taken off, there is a greater risk than existed before its use. You have only to wear a "wrist protector" for a day or two to realise how weak your wrist has become in the process.

I am personally an enthusiast for weight training; it is a fast, effective method of improving muscle strength and bulk, but simply putting on a weightlifter's belt does not make a weightlifter. It is far safer and more permanent to reduce lifting hazards by utilising ergonomic principles, such as keeping loads off the floor, reducing weight or using lifting equipment etc., and training workers to lift correctly.

Hoists and Scissors Jacks do not get back injuries! The most comprehensive back injury prevention training program costs less than one back injury. Correcting the cause of the problem is the obvious solution, not treating the symptoms by protective equipment which never ends.

Any apparent benefits for materials handlers wearing belts can be attributed to the restrictions imposed on bending forward, or twisting whilst working and perhaps reminding the worker to lift correctly. Against that must be weighed the fact that it will produce more problems than it solves in belts being too tight or too loose, getting lost, exchanged, stolen, damaged, stretched, not used or over used (worn all the time), their discomfort and unpopularity among women operators, and creating an unnecessary and unwanted supervisory responsibility.

If the demand for belts becomes too strident, either through the workers themselves or the unions, then I am of the opinion that the operator should buy it himself. Management must resist endorsing a practice which is not in the workers' best interests and, in fact, is roundly condemned by the majority of medical practitioners.

A recent qualified research project was carried out jointly by American Airlines and the Industrial Engineering Department of Texas University on 642 baggage handlers over an 8 month period in the use of back belts. It found no significant differences for the total lumbar injury incident rate or lost work days than the control group without belts. Indeed the groups who wore the belts for a while and then discontinued it had a higher lost day case injury rate than the other groups.

Fifty eight per cent of the participants in the test discontinued use of the belt before the end of the experiment, complaining it was too hot and it produced profuse sweating. It also rubbed, pinched and bruised ribs. The paper concluded: "Results indicate that the use of belts may, in fact, increase the risk of injury when not wearing a belt following a period of wearing a belt. Based on these results, the weightlifting belt used for this study cannot be recommended for use as an aid for lifting during the daily work activities of baggage handlers". (Congleton, J.J. et al. Texas A & M Univ. Ind. Eng. Dept. U.S.A. J. App. Erg. No.5, Oct.1992.)

Chapter 11
GOOD AND BAD EXERCISES

No element of the treatment of low back pain has provoked more controversy than exercise. The question of whether it is better to do only those exercises which bend the back backwards (extension) or forwards (flexion) is still unresolved and contentious, both in theory and practice. A great deal of research is available to justify both theories, and it will no doubt continue to stimulate its protagonists until a new modality appears.

It is not an objective of this book to analyse this or that treatment for low back pain, and making recommendations is even more presumptious in the light of the variations and reasons for back pain. Each case must be assessed on its merits. In Chapter 13 for instance, I discuss a significant research project indicating that the criteria for recurring industrial back pain turns out to be, not the treatment at all, but whether the subjects liked their job and whether the supervisor had a high regard for the worker concerned.

I am more involved with prevention and the fundamentals of biomechanical support for the spine. As you will have now read, this is to some degree dependent on good intra-abdominal pressure and the quality of the abdominal muscles; therefore, flexion exercises in lying with knees bent both before and after a back injury are important constituents of any preventive maintenance exercise regime.

Fig.66. Touching your toes with straight legs serves no purpose.

Fig.67a. The "Sit Up" with straight legs and attempting to get your head to your knees is worse.

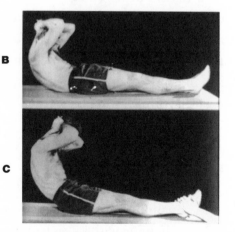

Fig.67b. The "Sit Up" as far as you can go with the abdominal muscles.
Fig.67c. The inner range limit of the abdominal muscles. The hip joints continue the movement.

Of course, this must be considered only as part of the overall rehabilitation programme, which I presume your doctor will be supervising. A good rule of thumb is that in the presence of an acute back condition, if any voluntary exercise either in flexion or extension is really painful, leave it alone, you are going too far, too soon.

All exercises are good; some are better than others, but there are *two* exercises I do not recommend. The first is touching your toes with straight legs (Fig. 66). You can live a long and very useful life without ever touching your toes with straight legs. I cannot understand the fascination for this exercise. There appears to be some kind of mystical relationship between being able to do this exercise and physical fitness. In fact, it has nothing whatsoever to do with fitness. I have seen smart, self styled "tough" guys demonstrate this as though they had just been declared Mr. Universe. All they are proving is that they have loose hamstring muscles at the back of their thighs. I have often wondered whether a few other things are also loose, which have no relationship to muscles!

The other exercise is "the sit up", touching your toes in the lying position with straight legs. (Fig. 67a,b,c.) The futility of this movement is that it is generally performed as an abdominal exercise. This is correct, but only until the spine reaches a right angle to the legs, after that the trunk will fall over of its own accord by gravity and the back muscles will act merely to steady the fall. Not only do the abdominals cease working beyond 90 degrees, but the stress on the posterior ligament of the spine, due to the ballistic bouncing of the trunk on the knees, stretches both the hamstring muscles and the narrow posterior lumbar ligament. There is nothing wrong with stretching your hamstrings, but it does not follow for the posterior ligament.

We have dealt with ligaments in some detail, and you may remember they are the joint defenders, precisely because they

Fig.68.

Peek Ups
Lying on back, slowly
curl head and shoul-
ders forward to look at
the feet. Hold 4-5
seconds and lower.

Fig.69.

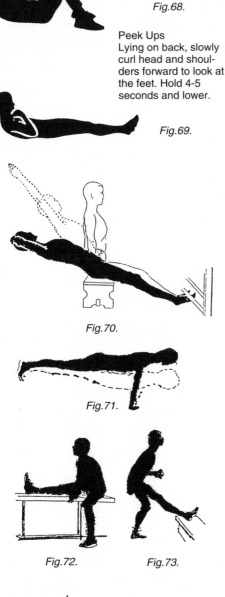

Fig.70.

Fig.71.

Fig.72.   Fig.73.

Achilles and Calf
Stretch
a) Achilles: Lean
against wall. Bend front
leg and keep back leg
straight. Press the heel
gently to the ground.
Repeat 3-4 times and
alternate.
b) Calf: Repeat above
BUT bend the back leg
slightly before pressing
down heal.

Fig.74.

are inelastic guy ropes, but if you stretch them to extremes in adult life because you desire a greater than normal functional range of movement, they will remain stretched at the expense of stability. In the process, you may have weakened an important defence mechanism, such as the posterior ligament of the spine.

If you are going to do "sit-ups" and you insist on putting your head on your knees, then bend your knees. The difference in exercise value is marginal (Fig. 68), but it is much safer for your spine. The strength of this popular exercise can then be graduated if necessary by increasing the length of the trunk, e.g. putting your hands above your head, or holding a weight behind the neck and getting someone to hold your feet down. There are many good abdominal exercises, of which Figs. 69, 70, and 71 are examples, but it would be advisable to check with your doctor before attempting them.

For those of you who do "sit-ups" as a hamstring stretching exercise, there are many exercises that will do this without prejudicing your spine, as illustrated in Figs. 72, 73 and 74.

After reading this statement, you may say, "if you should never touch your toes with straight legs, how come ballet dancers and gymnasts do it without any apparent ill effects?" The answer is, we are not discussing ballet dancers or gymnasts but you and I, which is a totally different matter.

Let me explain. At birth, the ligaments are soft and elastic, which allows the foetus to conform to the shape of the birth canal. After birth and consistent with growth development, the ligaments gradually lose their elastic quality and become firm but flexible structures, in order to carry out their function of guarding the joints and preventing dislocation. After adolescence, when growth has stopped, the length of the ligaments will be consistent with the range of movement you have elected.

Fig. 75.

Fig. 76. Long loose ligaments enable joints to do all sorts of things.

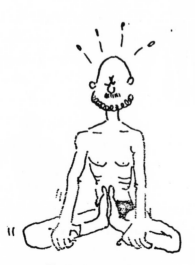

Fig. 77. It generally hurts.

As a baby, it was not difficult to put your foot in your mouth, your joints allowed that quite easily (Fig. 75). Yet, why is it so difficult now? The reason is you stopped doing it. Had you continued this activity into adult life, your ligaments would have simply stretched and grown proportionately longer to permanently accommodate this range of movement. The skeletal system consisting of bones, muscles and ligaments are very economic structures, whose performance depends on function. If you don't use it, you lose it, which is why ballet dancers start about the age of three, and serious gymnasts at five, and circus acrobats are in family dynasties, where the children are encouraged to maintain the fullest possible range of joint movement into adult life.

As has been mentioned before, if ligaments are loose and long, they cannot be as effective at guarding the joints, and dislocation becomes more likely. Some common gymnastic feats are, in fact, dislocations. The "Crucifix" exercise on the rings is an example that comes to mind and so is the "Splits," but here the muscles are powerful enough to act as ligaments and bring the joints back into correct alignment by sheer strength. The dislocation of a joint may not be painful if the ligaments are long and loose enough to accommodate it. The term "double jointed" is obviously a fallacy, you cannot have a double set of joints! (Fig. 76)

In a normal joint, dislocation would be preceded by tearing the ligaments, which accounts for the acute pain. It is also the reason why you cannot suddenly take up yoga at the age of 50, and sit there with your legs around your neck contemplating your navel without pain. There is nothing particularly wrong doing that providing you enjoy a bit of masochism, but expect it to hurt! (Fig. 77).

The next page illustrates an abdominal exercise routine I recommend and do myself, but if you intend to try them show the exercises to your doctor first, as you may have other problems, for which they might be contra-indicated.

SUGGESTED EXERCISES

Check with your doctor before accepting them as suitable for your back condition.

1

Sit Ups
Bend knees and curl up to a seated position. Lower back and repeat.

2 Peek Ups
Lying on back, slowly curl head and shoulders forward to look at the feet. Hold 4-5 seconds and lower.

4 Twisting Sit-Ups
With hands behind head and knees bent, curl up and touch elbow to opposite knee.

3 Hip Twister
Supported from behind, bend knees to chest and rock to each side.

6 Single Leg Extensions
Support from behind and alternate single leg extensions forward.

5 Hump and Hollow
On your hands and knees, relax your abdomen and let your back sag downward. Then hump your back. Repeat.

7

8 Pelvic Tilt
Lie on your back with your knees bent, feet flat on the floor and arms at your sides. Tighten your stomach muscles and flatten the small of your back against the floor without pushing down on the feet. Hold for five seconds, then slowly relax.

Pike and Tuck
Supported from behind, bring knees to chest and extend both legs right to pike position. Tuck knees back to chest in centre and extend legs to other side.

WHAT IS THE BEST SPORT FOR THE BACK?

Physical fitness, particularly of the abdominal and back muscles, is an important element of the spine's ability to cope with stress, and a specific individual exercise regime may be advisable. However, adopting a sport that suits you and is pleasant is more objective than static exercise, and you will also work much harder at it. Of course, being able to manage both is even better.

Before a back injury, almost any sport that extends you and improves your stamina, mobility and strength is good. After a back injury, it is advisable to select an activity with your doctor's advice that will not prejudice your back problem. Some sports in this regard are better than others. It is worth noting that strictly speaking, physical activity should not exacerbate back pain. Increased pain is always a signal that you are going too far or doing too much; however, if you do not entertain ideas of Olympic grandeur and are modest in your objectives, you can participate in most sports. My preference after a back injury is as follows:-

Swimming

At any time, but particularly after a painful back episode, swimming should be the activity of choice a soon as possible. Swimming is considered to be ergonomically the almost perfect sport for work done against energy expended. In swimming the water is supporting and the extension angle the spine adopts is good. This is in sharp contrast to the flexion posture of cycling. Swimming is also a very safe activity both for the muscular and cardio-vascular systems, and its mobilising value for a stiff back is great.

However, I do not consider swimming as doing a width of the pool and then watching the scenery for an hour! Rather, it is completing anything from 12 to 20 lengths in good time and leaving the pool with a feeling that you could not have gone much further. In my opinion, it should form a three times weekly element of any rehabilitation regime.

Walking
Every bit as good as jogging, and perhaps even better is fast walking. However, there is a very significant difference between relaxed walking, which is nice but has limited exercise value, and walking from A to B at a fast clip. For exercise to elicit a response from the muscular or cardio-vascular system, there must be potential to extend either system to its near limit. Relaxed walking requires very little effort and is virtually all momentum. I am referring here to fast serious walking done in a given competitive time if it is to be considered an exercise.

Jogging
An excellent recommended activity, despite those who feel that the jarring of the spine occasioned by this sport offsets the benefits in fitness. I do not accept this. The spine is well adapted to absorb normal vibrations of this magnitude, without suffering any ill effects, and providing you run in good running shoes, the physical gain is immeasurable.

Incidentally, it does not matter whether the shoes have one stripe or four stripes. What is important is that the shoes are comfortable, have a good flexible sole of reasonable depth, a heel 12mm to 15mm (1/2" to 1/4") thicker than the sole, padding for the Achilles tendon at the back, no rough seams on the inside, and preferably offer some ankle protection. Many aches and pains developed by runners come from unexpected stress due to biomechanical faults of the foot. Equally, some feet are difficult to fit because of a particularly high instep or a very broad foot, and customised shoes may be the only option.

Sex
A good functional activity for your back is sex in any position! Anything which takes your mind off a painful back whilst

mobilising it, must be worthwhile! When should you do it? Begin with three times a day after meals, and increase as often as you feel like it!!

Chapter 12

THE ERGONOMICS OF MATERIALS HANDLING

Despite the technical advances in robots and automation during the last decade and an equivalent rise in production, back injury resulting from materials handling has continued to be industries' worst accident statistic, both in severity and frequency.

One of the problems is that, although there are authoritative guidelines and recommendations on maximum lifting loads from agencies, such as OSHA in the U.S.A., the Health and Safety Commission in Great Britian, the Draft Code on Safe Manual Handling from Australia and others, operators are still expected to lift loads well in excess of established limits. It appears that awareness of the link between back pain and the repetitive lifting task is one thing, the economic packaging of products is another.

The practice continues, because the wealth of most countries rely on imports and exports and the manufacture of products from mechanical and electrical appliances to bagged material like flour, salt, peanuts or plastic, cannot be economically subordinated to comply with recommended lifting standards, unless the standards become international and enforced. Inevitably, much of the imported goods arrives in containers packed without consideration for the human element that will have to unload them (Fig. 78a).

Fig.78a. Imported sacks of plastic. Approximate weight 79lbs. (36kg.)

Throughout the world, there continues to be thousands of

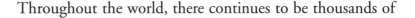

Fig.78b. Try telling this operator to bend her knees.

small industrial undertakings which do not see the advantages of mechanical handling equipment in human terms, who are manufacturing products that vary in size, shape and weight with a frequency and pace that makes it unrealistic to expect an operator to adopt a variety of lifting techniques. The stereotype response to a weight is to lift it, and it is the difference between theory and practice.

Only the practical application of ergonomics to materials handling will bridge this gap.

Unfortunately, words are not enough to change the reality of a badly designed work environment. You can train people to lift safely, but if they cannot do it because the work environment or the task by its design won't let them, you will achieve nothing except frustration, your sincerity will be questioned and you are wasting everybody's time (Fig. 78b).

Some years ago, I was commissioned to put in a back injury control programme at one of the largest aluminium smelters in the U.S.A. In a project of this type, it is necessary to teach correct lifting to all the workforce, regardless of any shift system which may be in operation, and inevitably, I found myself speaking to a "graveyard" shift at 2.00 in the morning.

Here were about 30 tired, hungry and dirty workers, whose only thoughts I am sure was to go home, have a bath and go to bed. To do them justice they participated in my lecture demonstration with interest, even if little enthusiasm. Finally, it was time to go and they all walked noisily out closing the door behind them. Four of the group, however, remained behind.

They approached me and, with what I can only describe as cold fury, began to berate me for recommending correct lifting techniques when as they put it "there was no damn way in the world they were going to be able to apply it on their worksite" and "why the hell . . . . don't you come over and take a look before going into all this stuff!" I explained it wasn't easy at 2.00a.m. in the morning to view every operation, but I would certainly go and take a look next day before I began lecturing.

The next day, I went to see the operation. The task consisted of laying a temporary floor of perforated iron or metal plates, each plate weighed approximately 158Kg (350lbs). The location was a keyhole aperture on the third floor of a four storey building. The plates arrived via a hoist outside the building, which serviced each floor, and were at this point pulled in, unhooked, carried and placed one at a time in position, in an area in which the workers were unable to stand upright. The task was only possible by using two men to lift every plate; this meant each man lifting 79Kg (175lbs) 26 times a day.

I was shocked. Of course, they all had back problems, who wouldn't! There were many economic, common sense design modifications that could have improved this task, like transferring the plates at the point of entry to a rail system similar to those used in moving sides of meat in butcher shops, or perhaps making the plates of a much lighter alloy, or even redefining the task as four man operation with a system of removable handles, but no attempts at modification had been made. Here now were four very uptight, recurring bad back employees costing the plant something in the region of $450,000 a year in lost time and medical bills.

It was a bad materials handling operation, and I expressed this, adding that I was immediately going to speak to the engineers about ergonomic modifications that would improve the situation. Whatever your intentions about the hazards of a task, do not "kid" the workers about it's safety, they generally know a phony at 50ft. You may not be in a position to do anything about it, a solution may be uneconomic or interfere with other operations in the plant, but if this is the case, then say so. Workers are well aware of safety problems and will co-operate, providing you are forthright and honest about it.

I saw the engineers and explained the problem. They thought about it for a minute or two and then informed me that it was one of many such problems, and would be considered in turn, which at the moment was half way down a priority list and about three months away.

This was the last thing I wanted to hear and it now became a full scale confrontation. I carefully described what their reply meant in human terms. Firstly, if any of those operators went to see a doctor about their back, they had only to describe their job to elicit the traditional medical officers reply of "I'm going to take you off this job for a while". That would be almost the basic medical response.

Secondly, if I am going to put in a back injury control programme, my advice for preventing back injuries would sound like a bad joke whilst such conditions existed, and undoubtedly would be another the laugh of the day around the cafeteria table.

Finally, if any of the operators wanted to go further and seek compensation, generally of the magnitude of a war reparation bill, I can see an attorney in court, crying to a jury (half of whom are probably back cases themselves), describing this job, the suffering, the indifference and now the permanent resulting disability. At this time there is only one option open to you, leave your check book in court, go home, and cut your wrists!

The point I am trying to establish with this story is that management has got to show that it cares about safety, even when it means the urgent redesign of an operation. Anything

Words will not change the reality of a badly designed work environment.

less, is not only bad industrial relations, but you could also be looking at half a million dollars or more compensation, plus whatever else it does to those insurance premiums next year. Of course, you may be self insured, which in any event means you had better reduce your back injuries to a minimum, or show a loss over conventional insurance.

I conclude this story as it began, "WORDS WILL NOT CHANGE THE REALITY OF A BADLY DESIGNED WORK ENVIRONMENT".

There are two broad principles to effective back injury control. Firstly, teach the workforce to take care of their backs by using their knees whenever they go towards the floor. Secondly, and more importantly, design out back hazards from the work environment wherever possible by utilising practical ergonomics.

A PROGRAMME FOR CONTROLLING INDUSTRIAL BACK INJURIES

Part 1. Teach the workforce safe lifting and bending, and make it possible for this instruction to be carried out in their work environment.

Part 2. Apply Ergonomics to the design of materials handling tasks.

Part 1
TRAINING OBJECTIVES

A.   Show the workforce the urgency and simplicity of elementary back care, without producing an increased sensitivity or apprehension about manual lifting and carrying.
B.   Develop an awareness towards back injury prevention that recognises off-the-job back hazards as being equally conducive to producing a back injury as the workplace itself.

C.   Show the workforce why back injuries are largely the product of mechanical wear and tear, accelerated by poor work postures, lifting and carrying, or bending and stretching regardless of the weight being lifted. (The process of degeneration).

D.   Motivate the workforce to accept a personal responsibility and commitment to preventing back injuries.

Training the workforce

Optimum size of class for training should not exceed 50 if good rapport is to be established and any questions dealt with adequately.

Time required: - a minimum of 30 minutes for essential elements to be covered.

The training communication should give priority to the following:-

Structure of spine in simple terms. Discuss spinal function of support for the skeleton, protection for the spinal cord and mobility. Show how ligaments and muscles support the spine but, in bending with straight legs using the back like a crane, it is only a very narrow ligament (the posterior ligament), plus the back muscles that hold the spine and prevents collapse.

Use analogy of discs as shock absorbing springs between the vertebrae. When the springs wear and the tension is lost, the disc narrows and bony surfaces are eroded, particularly the facet joints.

Demonstrate the mechanics of lifting using a bar or broomstick and a 10lb weight. Relate it to the spine as a 10 to 1 lever, proving that a 50lb lift using the spine represents a stress of 1500lbs (including the weight of the trunk). Show how using the thighs to lift eliminates all spinal stress, is easier and is the "natural" way of bending used by infants and weightlifters.

Talk about why people don't do it; most people lift in the simplest way using only their hip joints, which is a short cut to the floor. Emphasise the "golfers lift" as a much safer alternative always supporting the trunk on whatever is within reach, or kneeling on one knee to put the load across the knee and then standing up by pushing off the rear leg.

Comment on awareness versus performance and the tendency to underestimate "natural lifting", because it is so simple.

Be constructive, "you can lift any reasonable weight" (up to one third your bodyweight if not obese), providing you use your knees to do the work.

Encourage a positive commitment to safe lifting,
"Help us to make this programme a success".
"We are not trying to sell you anything but common sense",
"It's up you, we can only show you and tell you".
"The spine is a wonderful piece of human engineering but like everything else, it wears out, don't hurry it along".

You will need an articulated vertebrae and some simple anatomical slides.

If time permits, discuss off-the-job back injury prevention, using material from Chapter 15.

At this time, it is worth encouraging suggestions from the audience on how they might reduce lifting hazards in their immediate environment.

It is also necessary for managers and supervisors to be aware of correct lifting methods, so that they can set an example. For this reason, they should be present when addressing their workforce. Their responsibility also includes reinforcing the training programme, and looking for ergonomic solutions to materials handling problems.

A

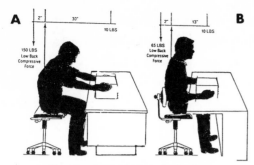

Keep loads as close to the body as
possible during lifting.
Recommend keeping loads under
10lbs. for seated work tasks.

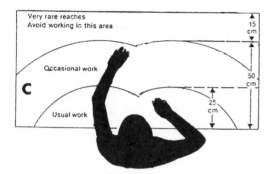

Figs.79a, b, c. Work bench or
desk dimensional work limits.

"Not this"

Figs.80. The height of an internal
risor with provision to rest either leg.

B *Part 2*

THE ERGONOMICS OF MATERIALS HANDLING.

The second element is to give managers, engineers and supervisors a different perspective from which to view materials handling tasks, and to make management personnel aware of the back stress resulting from poor work postures, inappropriate equipment and bad work design. There are seven check list ergonomic principles to be considered.

1. Decide whether the operator should be seated or standing

It is reliably estimated that at least 20% of all standing operations can be just as efficiently done seated. The operator's seated position should ensure that the task is performed in an area encompassed by an arc approximately 10" (250mm.) from the front edge of the table or desk to the extended right and left arm of the operator. Figs. 79a,b,c, clearly demonstrates the biomechanical reasons for this recommendation.

The area 10" to 20" (250 to 500mm.) from the front edge requires an undesirable degree of trunk flexion and encourages poor occupational postures. It should only be used for occasional work. A work bench or desk over 24" (600mm.) is therefore a waste of timber, unless there is a sound specific reason for the extra depth.

If a standing position is unavoidable, ensure that a suitable footrail is available. The supporting tie or other bracing under a bench including a shelf is not an acceptable footrest, invariably it is neither the right height nor is it supportive enough. The correct height for this type of support should be slightly less than the riser of an internal stair and be 5" to 6" (125 to 150mm.). Provision should also be made for resting either foot (Fig. 80.)

The reason for this feature is interesting. The curve of the lumbar spine is maintained by a guy rope principle, utilising

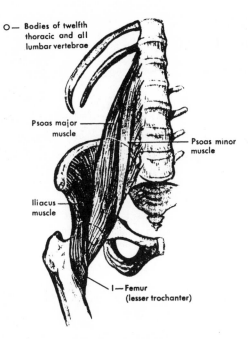

O — Bodies of twelfth thoracic and all lumbar vertebrae

Psoas major muscle

Psoas minor muscle

Iliacus muscle

I — Femur (lesser trochanter)

Figs.81. Iliopsoas
From the front and sides of the lumbar vertebrae
to just below the neck of the Femur.

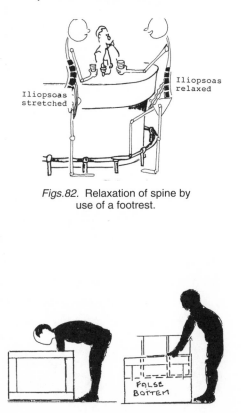

Iliopsoas stretched

Iliopsoas relaxed

Figs.82. Relaxation of spine by
use of a footrest.

Fig.85. Raise the level of crates, use
empty boxes or a removable shelf.

FALSE BOTTEM

the lower back muscles of the spine as one guy rope, and the other by a muscle (iliopsoas) attached to the front and sides of all the lumbar vertebrae within the abdominal cavity. It then passes through the abdomen and finally wraps itself around the neck of the femur to be attached a little way down at the back of bone. (Fig.81.)

When it contracts it flexes the hip joint, and raises the leg, but in a standing position, it exerts a pull on the lumbar vertebrae and is thus able to maintain an equalising tension to the back muscles of the lumbar area. You have only to stand with your feet braced back to feel the powerful pull this muscle exerts on the lower back. This explains why it is so comfortable to put your feet up on a stool or a pillow under your knees when your back starts aching. Of course, every drinking bar in the country has known this for years! (Fig. 82.)

2. Get the load off the floor

Beginning a lift 15" (380mm.) to 18" (460mm.) off the floor (knuckle height) reduces the possibility of a back injury by as much as two thirds. Use pallets, ramps, platforms etc. Don't put things on the floor, somebody, and it may be you, will have to pick it up and will be at risk. (Figs. 83, 84, 85 and 86.)

Shoulder Hgt.
50" (1270 mm.)

Knuckle Hgt
20" (508 mm.)

Knee Hgt
18" (457 mm.)

Fig.83. All lifts should be
within these limits.

Fig.84. Get it off the floor

Fig.86. Not good.   Much better!

Fig.87. This operator is repetitively in this posture. Frames are taken from the electroplating shop, down the ramp (right) and are left on the floor.

Fig.88. It was a simple matter to replace the partition separating the operator from the electroplating shop with a platfrom at knee height to remove the postural stress from the task. Note how much easier it is for the delivery of the racks on one level.

Fig.89. The material in this crate are boxes of gears weighing approximately 85lbs. (38.5kg.) Some of them will be at ground level, using his legs to lift would be impossible.

Fig.90a. By restructuring their delivery on line from inward goods by pallet and making a platform of five pallets to put it on, the operator can walk around any side and lift from a convenient height. A fork hoist will maintain the pallets at the correct height.

Fig.90b. The half crate with detachable sides is a viable option to Fig.89. above left.

The most universal, the worst, and the most easily corrected materials handling problem in industry today is the amount of material placed at floor level, when all around are pallets piled up to the roof and not being used. Two pallets can reduce the degree of bending to knee level, and reduce the hazard at the same time by 65%. Put your unused pallets to work!!! (Fig. 91.)

Fig.91. Stored pallets doing nothing, whilst these tins of paint are a lifting hazard. Two tiers of tins is regulation in this plant. Note, condition of pallets.

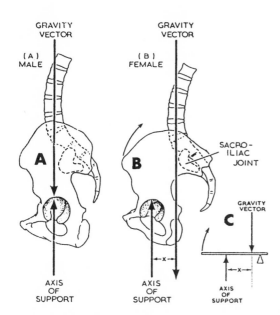

Fig.92. (A) In the male, the weight of the body (and also anything carried) is vertically above the upward thrust between the legs (B) In the female, body weight falls behind the axis of support which, being at a greater distance from the pivot through the sacro-iliac joints, tends to rotate the pelvis. This is shown diagrammatically in (C).

Nothing demonstrates the necessity for getting weights off the floor better than an anatomical difference between males and females, that puts females at a mechanical disadvantage in lifting. Males and females of approximately the same stature may be subject to different stresses when handling the same object, because of the biomechanical differences between the sexes in the pelvic region.

The hip sockets in the male are located directly under the bodies of the lumbar vertebrae and in the same plane as the centre of gravity (Fig.92a,b,c). In the female, they are located further forward, resulting theoretically in an apparently longer spine. The calculated effect of this, is that any object

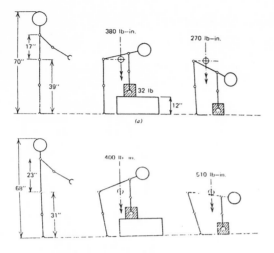

Fig.93. Females are at a significant mechanical disadvantage at low lifting levels.

Fig.94. A knee high platform or two pallets would make this task considerably easier on her spine!

handled by women would appear to be approximately 15% heavier than if the same object were handled by a man of identical stature.

The hypothesis requires further research, but there is every indication at present that whilst females are at a mechanical disadvantage lifting from the floor, a pallet or platform 12" to 14" (300 to 350mm.) high minimises this sex difference (Fig. 93.) (E. Tichauer, N.Y.Univ.1973), and is another reason why handling weights and other related activities should not be done from floor level, particularly with straight legs. (Fig.94.)

This is not intended to indicate that there should be some sort of sex discrimination in materials handling, but rather to emphasis that the human spine as our equipment for lifting weights is fallacious; it wears out, it gets diseases, it must be clothed and fed and it has a low stress tolerance, even a simple crowbar does a better job.

What I am saying is that in a technological age that can take us to the moon, surely we can structure materials handling environments that are not hazardous for anybody, male or female. The irony is that such equipment is available, the problem is getting industry to realise that in the long run it is economic common sense and good management.

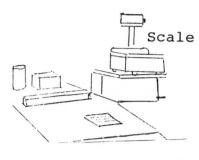

A A supermarket scale should be at counter level.

3. Minimise the distance the load is carried either in walking or lifting

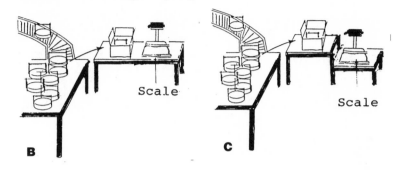

B　　　　　**C**

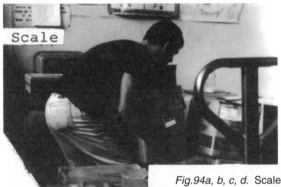

D

Fig.94a, b, c, d. Scales should be placed so that lifting products up to them is eliminated.

Fig.95. Platforms, Racks or Trolleys used for stacking and moving loads should, wherever possible be of a uniform height.

Fig.96. Walking with loads above 25lbs. (11.5kg.) should be minimised or eliminated by the introduction of suitable hoists or trolleys.

Fig.97. this female operator walks 60ft. (18m.) with a 100lb (45kg.) load from a holding bay. A trolley should be used.

There should be no walking up stairs or ladders with weights in excess of 20lbs. (9kg).

Fig.98. 100lbs (45kg.) sack of plastic taken up stairs with a rise of 12" (300mm.) The operation should have utilised a gravity fed hopper.

Fig.99. The first step is 14' (350mm.) high. The sacks weigh 60lbs. (27kg). A ground level elevator taking opened sacks up to the hopper is indicated.

Fig.100. Carrying a bin of industrial waste weighing 72lb (33kg,) up a flight of 18 stairs is ridiculous. A platform elevator would be more economical and safer.

4. Reduce the weight. (Figs. 101, 102.)

It is easier and safer to do two lifts of 25lbs. (11.5kg.) than one lift of 50lbs. (22.5kg.)

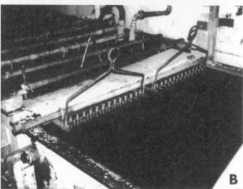

Fig.101. These frames, 76lb (34kg) were pulled through electroplating vats. A standard for pulling is Males 40lb (18kg.) Females 30lb (13.6kg.) Halving the weight made a difference.

Fig.102. If a repetitive lift cannot be reduced to 40lb (18kg) then make it 400lbs (182kg) so that no one will be tempted to lift it!

Fig.104. This container weighed 40lbs (18kg.) and because it has only one handle it can only be lifted using one hand. If the handles were two horizontal grips on opposite sides, a two handed lift would be adopted.

Fig.105. The push required to overcome the inertia of a stationary load on a trolley is approximately 10% of its up weight. The loaded weight of this trolley was 3,000lbs. (1,360kg.) It is no longer a trolley, it is now the S.S. "Queen Mary"!

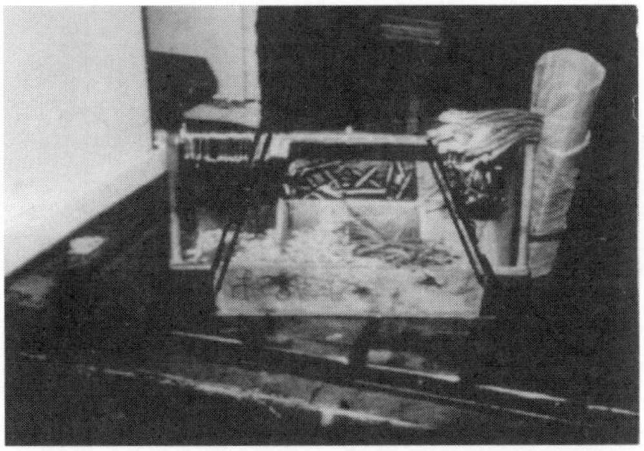

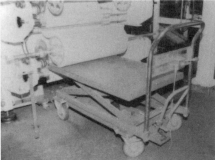

Fig.106. A mechanics maintainence kit with a one week supply of spare parts. Again by its shape it is a one handed lift. This was avoidable by shortening the box along the lines shown. 3 days supply in a smaller box was raedily adopted with satisfaction all round.

5. Redesign the container. (Figs.103, 104, 105, 106.)

Utilise handles (either fixed or portable), for containers to give operators a centre of gravity that is low and close to the body.

Fig.103. Hand grips can make all the difference.

6. Use equipment for materials handling, not operators. (Figs. 107, 108.)

Scissor, Jacks, Cranes, Hoists, Elevators and even Crowbars are better than spines for moving material, and in the end more efficient and economical. If you avoid buying equipment that is necessary for materials handling, you will pay for it inevitably in strains and sprains and back injuries, except it will cost you much more than the equipment would have cost in the first place and you will still need it.

Fig.107. A turntable scissors jack is portable, versatile and much more efficient than a human spine for materials handling. Estimated direct cost of a single back injury is $5,700 in U.S.A. (Pru. Ins.)

Fig.108. A trolley incorporating a scissors jack. This piece of equipment enabled the plastic sheeting roll to be taken from its storage rack and put on its machine without being lifted in any way.

Fig.109. I found this excellent hoist in "Salvage"

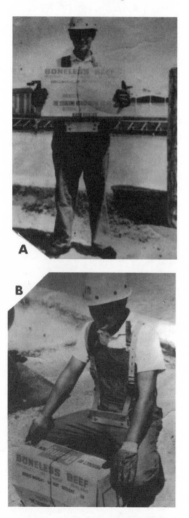

Fig.110. A workers suggestion for repetitive lifting for stevedores. It reduced back injuries by 50% The shelf on which the box rests is aluminium.

7. Any equipment used for lifting must be easier to handle than lifting by hand

Operators will not use cranes, hoists or any materials handling lifting equipment if it is more difficult in terms of manipulation or more time consuming than what they were doing previously. This is not only the stereotype response to the introduction of new equipment, but in a paced operation where production quotas are anticipated, workers will not tolerate the frustration. In summary, any modifications for lifting you are considering, must be easier and faster than lifting by hand or it will never be used. (Fig. 109).

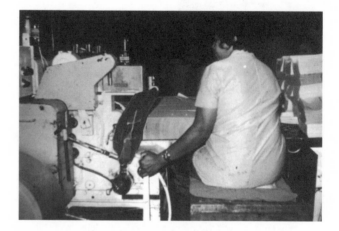

Fig.111. A piece of cardboard shaped like a banana leaf, and attached to an agitator becomes an effective fan for this island operator in a badly ventilated plant.

8. Utilise worker involvement in the design of work stations.

Discuss ergonomics and its objectives with the workforce to give direction to their ideas of a better, safer work environment and encourage their participation in the design process. I have yet to meet a worker who did not have at least three ideas on improving his or her task. Figs. 110 and 111)

There are several worthwhile advantages to this approach:-

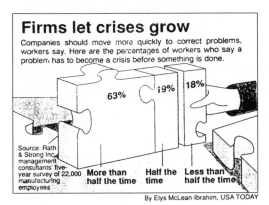

Firms let crises grow

Companies should move more quickly to correct problems, workers say. Here are the percentages of workers who say a problem has to become a crisis before something is done.

63% — More than half the time

19% — Half the time

18% — Less than half the time

Source: Rath & Strong Inc. management consultants' five-year survey of 22,000 manufacturing employees

By Elys McLean-Ibrahim, USA TODAY

Fig. 112. In my experience these figures are an underestimate.

1. You will be overwhelmed with suggestions, some of which will be impractical, but a few will be an improvement and one or two will be brilliant.
2. It is excellent industrial relations.
3. You will get full worker cooperation in whatever change is implemented.
4. It sends a clear message to the workforce that management does care. (Fig.112)

Part 3

Education helps, but the preferred method of control are engineering controls, because the primary focus of an ergonomic programme is to make the job fit the person, not force the person to fit the demands of the job.

Utilising the check list previously discussed, the following steps are recommended:-

1. Identify the person problems with a "worst first" approach; observe these jobs, decide where you think the problems are coming from and videotape the job.
2. Identify the risk factors, those parts of the job associated with ergonomic problems.
3. Propose alternatives which would eliminate or reduce the risk factors.
4. Interview workers doing the job and supervisors about possible solutions, e.g. is it necessary to lift it in the first place and, if so, does it have to be done manually?
   Can the distance carried or the height lifted be reduced?
   Can the container be improved?
   Can the operator get close to the lift and bend his or her knees?
   Should the lift be designated a "two man lift?"
   Will lifting equipment be an advantage in this situation?
5. Select the most appropriate alternative.
6. Implement chosen alternative.
7. Monitor the effects of the changes, and reinforce the

workers responsibility to lifting safely, via the instructions on "natural lifting".

A major success story in the application of ergonomic principles to materials handling tasks occurred at a railcar repair shop in Palestine, Texas, in 1986. The repair shop was noted for its high incidence of low back injuries. In 1985, 9 of 13 lost time injuries involved the low back, resulting in 579 lost work days and 194 restricted or limited work days. Absenteeism at the facility was 4%.

Safety professionals, management and line supervisors were trained in basic job evaluation and ergonomic design techniques, and corrective measures were taken. These included storing all tools and material off the ground between knee and shoulder height with the heaviest items at knuckle height; devising winches to lift and handle heavy equipment; and designing worktables, dollies, and carts to more easily handle heavy railway car parts and tools. Management took a participatory approach and encouraged workers to configure their own tools and material handling assists to make their tasks easier and safer.

By 1988, low back injuries and lost work days had fallen to zero and absenteeism had declined to 1%. In addition, productivity had risen by more than 85%, with no increase in staff size. The railroad calculated the cost-benefit ratio of this ergonomic effort to be approximately 1 to 10. (Human Factors Society Bulletin Vol.34. No.3. March 1991).

Chapter 13

"MALINGERERS"

A spectre haunts every safety manager in industry. It is the spectre of the back injury that occurs for no apparent reason and recurs at frequent indiscriminate intervals, equally for no apparent reason. Since the condition has few visible signs, there is a tendency for some people to assume it does not exist, and that the complaints are probably unjustified.

A conventional wisdom therefore prevails among some factory managers in industry, that you can really do very little for back pain, because "these days, many workers have a low pain threshold and are simply looking for time off". The result of such complacency is a philosophic resignation towards back injury where management regards back injury as a part of the price it must pay for production, and prevention programmes are considered to be of marginal value.

This attitude toward back injury is particularly prevalent among those who, by a fortuitous mixture of good spinal genetics, a cast iron constitution and a lot of luck, have never had a back problem. For them, work is the survival of the fittest, and they are always ready to inform you that workers today "have never had it so good!"

Of course, adopting this approach to back pain makes life much easier for the supervisor and poses its own solution — do nothing — because it doesn't matter anyway. Not only is this rationale patently absurd, but it is also self-defeating, and denies all the proven research on industrial back problems. When you believe back injuries are beyond your control, you inevitably create a cycle of high incidence, lost time and a lack of confidence and faith in your workforce. The most unfortunate effect is that it inhibits any constructive human factors approach to the problem, and it is negative management.

These attitudes are not only common but dangerous, especially in view of the fact that, if someone does not suffer a specific on-the-job back injury, the chances of developing a chronic back condition unrelated to the job are 3 to 1 after the age of 30; worse still, you immediately prejudice all the supposedly legitimate back sufferers, a figure reliably estimated to be 60% of the population.

Real malingerers are the ones who get time off for a back injury, but have nothing wrong with them. They stay at home, or are in the garden, paint the house, go fishing or take a trip to Bermuda. This category represents no more than 1% of the back injury spectrum. There are so few, it would be dignifying them unjustifiably to give them more than a passing reference.

Between this group and the next, there is another 25% of a category who indeed have mild back problems with which they could certainly continue to work, but choose not to because they have a low pain tolerance. This is their perogative.

Every back condition must be treated with seriousness and sympathy, or the large majority of genuine cases will be overlooked and the classic chronic back problem becomes initiated. I believe "alternative work" or "light duties" on a temporary basis ought to be available in every plant with a sizable work force. Unfortunately, many plants will not structure this kind of task arrangement, citing as a reason the low productive capacity of such work, and insurance companies who do not approve, on the assumption that you may convert a mild back injury into a severe one by continuing any kind of work activity, however light. The fact that it is excellent rehabilitation, is recommended by OSHA, and works very well indeed in many U.S. plants, particularly those who are self-insured, is studiously ignored.

It may be that some back problems are, in fact, a manifestation of a latent psychological problem, but telling a back sufferer it is not serious and it is all psychosomatic, is futile. The pain will not go away, and it does nothing to define the real problem. They may not need medical treatment, yet have a considerable need for psychological counselling or a change of work environment, but it does not make them malingerers.

Pain thresholds are very personal personality traits. I have seen tough commandoes faint at the sight of an injection needle, and professional wrestlers terrified at the prospect of having a tooth pulled.

I suggest two approaches that may help you to change an operator's attitude to back pain; the first is, in the event of a lost time injury, the operator is visited as soon as possible, and certainly no later than 24 hours by a sympathetic member of the Safety Committee, or the Occupational Nurse, or if possible, the supervisor, to assure the employee that management knows and cares. That he or she is missed, that their job is still there, and that their fellow workers care.

The visits are then continued at frequent intervals throughout the off-work period, and of course take a magazine or two and perhaps some fruit. Most workers respond magnificently when they know their contribution to the plant matters, and is appreciated. This is part of the human condition.

The second approach is to have a "doctor's day" in the plant. Most of the doctors seen by the workforce have little or no idea of the real pressures experienced by their patients in their working environment, the kind of loads they lifts, the pace of work, and whether alternative work is available. It would be of great assistance to a local G.P. to have a personal awareness of his patients' work environment if they are to manage a back injury with the patients' best interests in mind. For a large majority of back problems, bed rest or long periods off work is a deadly combination. One researcher, (McGill) found that a worker off for six months has only a 50% chance of ever returning to productive work again. Other researchers have put this figure as low as 35% (Rosen, N.B.)

A programme of this type for local doctors could be carried out in a morning or an afternoon with the doctors paid for their attendance, and possibly culminating or beginning with a luncheon address by the firm's Medical Officer, Safety Officer or Occupational Nurse discussing the firm's philosophy towards accidents, the "light work" options, followed by an in-depth tour of the plant.

Unfortunately, the easiest way to get time off work is to have a back injury. It doesn't require bandaging or injections, and will get you off anything or everything. What's more, it can be accounted for in any number of ways from a cough, to picking up a pencil. So, is it possible to determine whether a back pain is mild, major, or malingering? Muscular, ligamentous or both, degenerative or traumatic? Above all, is this the beginning of a prolonged back disability? The answer is "with a great deal of difficulty and educated guesswork". You need all the information you can get for a reliable overall assessment, and your first source is the accident report.

Most of the accident investigation forms I have seen appear to be designed to comply with the firm's record keeping obligations, rather than to assist the Medical Officer in the diagnosis and treatment of the injury. Sometimes the forms are not even taken seriously, with fatuous questions and answers, which I have seen, like: "why do you think it happened"? Answer: "it was an act of God", or "accidents happen". Such replies on an accident report form are a nonsense, which makes the exercise a total waste of everybody's time. If this is the degree of importance placed on accident investigation, do not be surprised when it is not taken seriously.

A good accident investigation system is central to any attempt at reducing back injuries, and its focal point is the initial accident reporting form, completed at the time and site of the accident.

For instance, it is vitally important to know whether the work environment was at fault, because of the weight or dimensions of the object lifted, and whether the human factors of the operator such as stature, obesity, or lack of fitness, was a contributing element. If you are trying to determine cause and effect, you need to know how far the load was carried, how high it was lifted, how much did it weigh and did the operator receive instruction on lifting and when. This is the essential information necessary for an objective assessment, yet it is rarely asked.

I believe it is important for workers to know that in their firm, everything possible is being done to avoid back injuries, but if it happens, it will be viewed as a serious accident, and the subsequent investigation will reflect that philosophy. It would be inadvisable of me to discuss the methods and tests available to determine the genuineness or otherwise of back pain and its functional disability, because techniques differ. Many aspects must be considered, and it is very much a question of medical and industrial experience.

Consideration must be given to whether or not the operator is likely to become a frequent low back problem, and the following list of factors should prove useful. (From the book

"Orthopaedic Problems at Work" by Dr. M. Laurens Rowe, M.D.)

RISK FACTORS FOR PROLONGED BACK DISABILITY

A. The Patient
1. Limited vocational assets (age, physical condition, education).
2. Poor work record, job dissatisfaction.
3. Frequent visits to medical department for minor complaints.
4. Frequent absences from work for minor conditions.
5. Language barrier.

B. The History of Injury
1. Exaggerated severity of injury incident. Blames others.
2. Anger toward Company or its representatives.
3. Dramatic description of symptoms
4. Inappropriate symptoms.
5. Past history of disabling low back pain, myelogram, surgery.

C. The Physical Examination
1. Eagerness for time off
2. Over-reaction to examination manoeuvres.
3. Inappropriate and inconsistent areas of tenderness.
4. Differences in findings when distracted or believed unobserved.
5. Complaint of severe aggravation of symptoms by the examination.

D. The Worksite
1. Heavy work. Limited opportunity for modified job transfer.
2. Inflexible, demanding supervision. Bias concerning backache.
3. Patient not popular with supervisors or co-workers.
4. Inappropriate benefit structure.

E. The Home
1. Over-protective spouse
2. Back disability useful in coping with marital problems.
3. Back disability useful in coping with parental problems.
4. Obsessive gardener
5. Job moonlighting

F. The Course of Treatment
1. Frequent changes of primary therapist.
2. Care in charge of inappropriate therapists.
3. Multiple consultations by physicians in same speciality.
4. Disparagement of therapists.
5. Visits to hospital emergency department with low back symptoms.
6. More than two surgeries.

Further food for thought is a longitudial prospective study carried out on 3,020 workers at the Boeing Aircraft Factory in Washington, with a 4 year follow up. Other than a history of current or recent back problems, the factors found to be most predictive of back injury reporting, were not any of the traditional reasons such as fitness, height, or weight of lift, but whether or not they enjoyed their job, whether their supervisor thought highly of them, and whether there was a previous history of back problems.

The paper concluded that: "A job that is perceived to be a burden, unenjoyable, unfulfilling, and providing few assets may strongly influence the readiness to report a back problem. Study of the relative contributions of physical and non-physical variable show that evaluations of back problems in industry that exclude these highly significant work perception and psychosocial variables are of limited value. (Bigos, S.J. "The Spine" Vol.16. No.1. P.1 to 6.)

Chapter 14
FURNITURE AND BACK PAIN

THE CHAIR

The influence of chairs on back pain, muscular stress, work satisfaction and productivity are now well documented areas of ergonomic research. In one survey of a 1,000 office workers, 54% declared that a comfortable chair was a major factor in influencing productivity. Concern for good work postures is forcing more attention than ever before to the design of furniture, both industrial and domestic. Of all the human needs in a work environment, good seating must be one of the most important.

This chapter sets out to underline some general principles derived from research into the design of good seating. It makes no claim for originality; the wheel has been invented! Its objective is, hopefully, to influence readers to look more critically at ergonomic data, and to give you, the buying public, a criteria for selecting more wisely and discerningly from the bewildering array of seats currently on the market.

Sitting down is a natural human posture. People sit down because they feel that sitting is less fatiguing than standing, but in many chair designs the opposite is more true. After a short period on some chairs, the unfortunate sitter finds it more comfortable to stand. Sitting can, in fact, be a tiring and painful experience on a poorly designed seat. For most of us, at least 50% of our waking lives is spent sitting on a chair. We sit to work, travel, watch T.V., converse. Yet for most of the population, the sole criteria of a "nice" chair is it's appearance.

Some time ago, the British magazine "Design" conducted an experiment in which eight people were blindfolded and asked to rank nine chairs in order of comfort. They were asked not to touch the chairs, but merely to sit on them. A week later, this time without the blindfolds they were asked to rank them again. They could now see the chairs before they sat in them. Result? Everyone changed their minds dramatically! Half the subjects altered their ranking by at least four places and only six of the 72 rankings were consistent. Closer to home, a few years ago a group of my final year Architecture students, who had previously been trained to evaluate chairs, made a tour of the largest furniture stores in the city and found that the best selling easy chair in every store, except one, was the one they had ranked bottom for comfort.

Factory Furniture

Industrial seating is particularly poor. It amazes me that office staff and certainly secretaries sit on relatively good chairs, which is as it should be, but the factory labour force who, in a manner of speaking, are the productive element of the work force, often have to sit on anything they can find, sometimes it is merely an old box. It should come as no surprise that many workers prefer to stand. The concept that production and comfort are irreconcilable, because the operator will go to sleep, only seems to apply to the factory labour force, despite the fact that it is a disproven and outdated concept. Many assembly type factory tasks could be done far more efficiently sitting, providing the seat was comfortable.

Comfort requirements

In recent years, serious doubts have grown about the quality of seats and whether they are suited for their purposes. Research in anatomy, physiology, biomechanics and orthopaedics is throwing more light on the physical problems associated with seating. However, despite all this accumulated knowledge which is freely available, seating remains poor. Some chairs look as though the designer had never seen

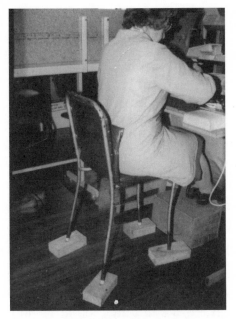

Fig.113. Sitting on whatever you can find.

Fig.114. "I would sooner stand"

a human body. They do not conform to body curves, they overload certain issues to the point of fatigue, and they do not support the hollow of the back. Most people are so accustomed to poor seating, they accept discomfort as a matter of course (Figs. 113, 114).

One chair cannot fit everybody, nor will it be suitable for every function. It is a mistake to buy a chair expecting it to be comfortable for a variety of tasks such as studying, dining or relaxing. It cannot, and a chair which tries to do all of these functions will end up doing none of them well. A chair should be purchased on the basis of whatever specific function it is going to be used for 75% of the time. If it turns out to be suitable for other activities, accept it as a fringe benefit and be grateful! Strictly speaking, a dining chair is not a typist's chair, and a work seat is not a cafeteria dining chair.

Whilst there are many claims for badly designed chairs producing all kinds of pathologies from disc degeneration to haemorrhoids, the truth is that there is no real evidence to support such claims. However, there is equally no doubt that chairs which offer little support for the spine force the sitter into bad postures, which can make an existing condition worse or precipitate the onset of a latent musculo-skeletal disorder.

Posture and Performance

The main purpose of a seat is not just to take the weight off the feet. It must also provide sufficient support to enable the sitter to maintain a stable posture, and be able to relax those muscles not directly required for the task. This principle applies whether the work is eating, typing, relaxing or sitting at a factory bench. A good chair does not attempt to hold the sitter in a particular posture. The ability to change position often is very important to delay fatigue. Quite small changes in position may be all that is necessary; for example, altering the angle of the knee with a foot flat on the floor. Akerblom,

Fig.115. Different sitting positions and back-rests. (a) The forward sunken sitting position. The dorsolumbar region takes the greatest strain and needs support more than the rest of the back. b) Correct back-rest. c) Chest support. d) Back-rest too high. e) Back-rest too upright. (After Schede and Akerblom)

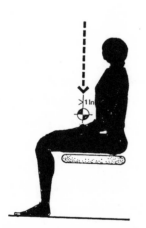

Fig.116. Centre of gravity of the upright seated figure.

one of the pioneers of ergonomic chair designs, says, "a good chair is one which permits as many good postures as possible being adopted without interference with the task. (Fig. 115).

Sitting Postures

Prolonged sitting in the same position usually leads to discomfort, with feelings of sheer tiredness in many instances building up such tension, that to move becomes compulsive. One of the reasons for this is that the centre of gravity for a seated human is about 1" (25mm) in front of the navel and, in order to relieve tension on the spine, one is either obliged to lean forward off the backrest or slide downwards and slump on the backrest. Studies of the postures people actually adopt show that they compromise by spending a fair proportion of the time with legs crossed leaning their arms on the table or on the arm rest. The reason for crossing legs is to lock the joints, in order to stabilise the various body segments. Reconciling the anatomical and physiological demands of seating with the aesthetic demands of the public is a frustrating exercise for most professional chair designers. (Fig. 116.)

Failure to apply the general principles of good seating causes discomfort and frustration which, in turn, affects concentration. Many plays and films would be infinitely less boring if the seats were more comfortable. Respecting these principles does not constrain a chair design, but enhances it. Good posture has been described as "the state of muscular and skeletal balance". Poor posture, on the other hand, is "a faulty relationship of the various parts of the body, which produces increased strain on supporting structures". At this point, it is important to stress that I am concerned not only with people who do not have any pathological problems, but also those in whom the effects of ageing have led to disorders which may make them more sensitive to long enforced postures and pressure on soft tissues.

The difference between theory and practice

Wishful thinking   Preferred body posture

Recommended and actual postures. The upright trunk posture required in many brochures and standards corresponds to 'Wishful thinking'.

The actual body posture mostly observed at VDT workstations.

Fig.117. Relaxed posture on an international telephone switch-board.

Design for differences

The world is not entirely made up of fit, young, athletic, mobile people, but also of ageing adults, whose circulation is not what it used to be, and with a reducing range of movement, who find getting in and out of some chairs difficult, if not impossible. Something like 10% of the adult population fall into this category.

There is also a substantial group of people with degenerative changes and functional disorders like Lumbago or Sciatica. There is an army of people with back problems who find almost any chair increases their pain and discomfort. We will see why presently, but it is time that furniture design was also examined from this point of view, not because it requires exceptional design considerations, but because any design that accommodates this group would be even more comfortable for the rest of the population.

Man is still not fully evolved to suit his upright position on what are phylogentically his hindfeet. The body of man is still only partially adjusted to its unique position on two legs. These facts are to some degree responsible for pain in childbirth, varicose veins, haemorrhoids, flat feet, degenerating discs and other ills. The invention of the chair on which to sit only complicates matters. When we bend two legs and sit upon the gluteal (seat) muscles of the buttocks on a raised seat, we are performing an action so new that it is not even common to all mankind. It is, therefore, essential that proper account be taken of the dimensionable variability of human beings.

Data available

Each dimension of a chair poses its own problems, but there is a wealth of published anthropometric (body measurement) data on which to draw. It is important, for instance, that the seat height is determined by the smallest stature, and seat width by the largest stature if it is to be suitable for the majority of the population. Exactly which "percentile" or portion of the population is to be regarded as the smallest or the largest is a problem for individual designers, who must be aware that there is no such thing as an "average person". No one is suggesting that research can lead to one ideally comfortable seat for all people and all purposes, but it has provided us with basic information about anatomy in sitting, about physiology and posture, and the range of human body dimensions which could make all chairs more comfortable without being necessarily more expensive.

There are many dimensions to a chair, but the five most important are:-
1. Seat Height.
2. Seat Angle.
3. Seat Padding.
4. Seat Depth.
5. Angle of the Backrest.

Seat Height

Of all the dimensions of seating, seat height is the most important. It would appear that many of the designers of chairs have assumed that the thighs should rest firmly on the seat so as to increase the weight bearing area, and distribute the pressure from the upper part of the body. Such a point of view must, however, be wrong. The soft tissues of the thighs cannot possibly provide such support (Fig.118). The only structure that can provide it is the bone itself. The weight of the leg alone is enough to compress the thigh to three quarters of its original width (Fig.119). Considerably less compression than this can have an injurious effect on muscles and nerves. The thigh is poorly adapted for even supporting its own weight, far less than 75% of trunk weight research indicates is transmitted through the seat.

In view of this, it is not surprising that people prefer to sit far forward on a seat with their weight resting on the ishial

Fig.118. Radiograph of normal thigh hanging freely

Fig.119. Radiograph of a thigh compressed by a high seat.

tuberosites, which are two bony projections below the pelvis, and thus relieve the pressure on the softer areas of the thigh.

Compression of the fleshy part also impedes and slows the circulation returning to the heart (Fig.120), blood then pools in the veins of the lower leg and with time may give rise to varicose veins. The thigh should be able to hang freely or only rest gently on the seat. To do this, the seat must be no higher than the length of the lower leg measured from the ground to 1" (25mm) below the cleft of the knee when the foot is flat on the floor and the knee at a right angle. An extreme view unsupported by scientific evidence is represented by Lin Yutang's dictum "the lower the chair, the more comfortable it becomes", which is why the toilet seat is probably the most comfortable in the house. Even 1" (25mm) makes a significant difference to comfort. Try it and see!

In fairness, the reluctance by manufacturers to reduce the basic height of chairs is partly the result of buyer resistance, which in turn is conditioned by the standard height of tables and desks. The present attitude of matching the chair to the table is absurd, when postural comfort begins with the chair. Nevertheless, seats can be, and are often, too low such as car seats. This posture forces extension on the lower leg, which in turn stretches the hamstrings at the back of the thighs and reduces the lumbar curve (Fig. 121a).

Unfortunately, lack of familiarity with chairs, desks and tables of smaller dimensions to which the research points, may give the impression they are out of scale, especially by direct comparison with existing items of furniture. However, if courageous manufacturers were to offer an option of a range of lowered height furniture, I believe it would not be long before the public would be appreciating and getting visually accustomed to lower heights with consequent advantages in comfort.

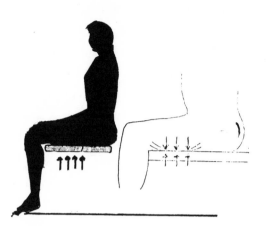

Fig.120. Seat too high, thigh is compressed.

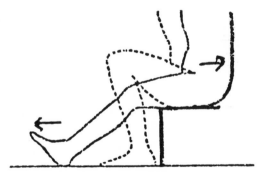

Fig.121a. Low chair reduces the lumbar curve and does not support the legs.

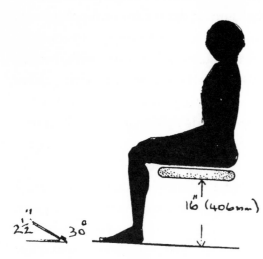

Fig. 121b. Seat height and footrest preferably adjustable.

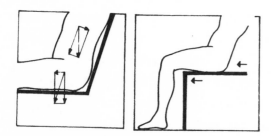

Fig. 122. The pressure on the back rest gives rise to an opposing force tending to push the buttocks forward if the seat is horizontal or less.

My recommendation are as follows:- Optimum seat height for a work chair 16" (406mm). All working seat heights should be adjustable over a range of 4$^1/_2$" (114mm), with a minimum height of 14" (355mm) and extending to a maximum of 18$^1/_2$" (470mm). The knees should be slightly higher than the hip joints, and if the seat is too high to permit this, a foot stool could be provided. Height of foot stool at the toes 2$^1/_2$" (65mm), Angle, approximately 30 degrees, preferably adjustable (Fig. 121b).

2. Seat Angle

A chair will not make a good seat if the seat angle is less than a right angle measured from the horizontal. We know that 75% of the body weight is taken by the seat, but this is proportional to the inclination of the backrest. If the seat angle is less than horizontal, that is, it tilts downward, more force is generated in the direction of sliding the buttocks forward (Fig. 122) creating a poor posture. This becomes even more intolerable when the seat surface is of polished timber or smooth vinyl and stability is further diminished.

An optimum angle for the lumbar support or back rest for a work chair is from 95 degrees to 105 degrees maximum, measured from the angle of the seat surface. If this is applied to a seat with a backward tilt of 5 to 7 degrees, the chair should be very comfortable with a nice, snug, well supported feel to it. However, for dining a horizontal seat is preferable, because of the necessity to lean forward to eat and converse. Whilst this is the best compromise, be aware it is a posture that is likely to reduce the hip angle to less than 90 degrees and compresses the hip joint making it uncomfortable with time, or very quickly for those with a hip joint dysfunction.

Restaurants take note! A 5 degree forward tilting seat may considerably improve a dining experience, providing the seat fabric offers sufficient resistance against sliding. This would be a distinct plus to any other amenity offered by the

Fig.123. The forward sloping seat. The essence of a "good" chair is the ability to change position easily and frequently. This chair does not meet the criteria.

restaurant. Fixed tables and chairs are not good design and the romantic booth with domed shape seats of slippery vinyl are often a disaster. I appeal to restaurant owners to consider the anthropometry of their clients and furniture with the care and consideration now reserved for the decor and the quality of the food. If they wish to retain a competitive edge in today's "dining out" culture, the first priority for comfortable dining must surely be the chair!

Many novel forward sloping chairs based on the original design developed by Danish surgeon Dr. Aage Chreston Mandal, (App.Erg. 1981. 12.1) are now available for some study and work tasks (Fig. 123). The designers claim it is less demanding on ligaments and, therefore, less fatiguing because of the redistribution of bodyweight over the centre of gravity. However, research on this chair carried out by Joan Ward, senior lecturer in the Department of Human Sciences, Loughborough University (J.Design. U.K. 333. P.33,) concluded that no experimental data on the use of the forward tilting seat had been offered to show that:-

(a)   The body weight is properly distributed over the seat surface.

(b)   Undue pressure is not exerted on the thighs.

(c)   Unnecessary muscular activity is not provoked by leaving the lumbar spine insupported.

(d)   The opportunity is available for minor and major changes of posture while working.

There were other complaints from Visual Display Terminal users and of difficulty of entry and egress from typists. (Drury and Francher, App. Erg. 1985. 16.1) Whilst the chair may be preferable for certain people on very short term tasks, I agree with the research conclusions and cannot recommend this type of chair.

3. Padding

Whilst a certain softness is desirable, it is also important that

111

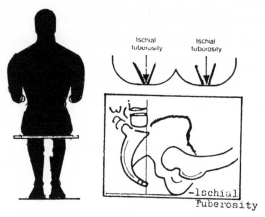

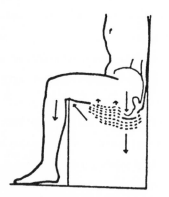

Fig.124. The ischial tuberosities and the structures in the area around them are designed to tolerate compression.

Fig.125. Upholstery too soft. Weight not taken by ischial tuberosities. It will produce circulatory discomfort and undue pressure from seat edge.

the seat be hard enough to concentrate pressures around the bones "ischial tuberosities", which accommodate this function. Soft tissue structure in this area are especially designed to cope with compression, without interfering with the blood supply (Fig. 124). In very soft seats, this function is diminished as pressure becomes more widely distributed into areas not designed for withstanding compression. For this reason, canvas chairs in quick time can become a pain in the bottom. For comfort, an average seat should have $1\frac{1}{2}$" (38mm) of medium foam padding over $\frac{1}{2}$" (12mm) of firm closed cell foam to prevent the sitter from "bottoming out". (Fig. 125).

Regardless of the type of chair, the front edge benefits from being softly padded to create a "waterfall" effect which helps to reduce pressure directly under the knee. You have only to sit in a deckchair for five minutes to experience this particular discomfort at its worst.

4. Seat depth

This dimension is usually taken from the back of the buttock to immediately behind the back of the calf. My impression of seat depth in current chair design is that most chairs are too deep for comfort. If a seat depth is more than 16" (406mm), then 50% of women will find the front edge of the seat pressing into their calves, forcing them to sit or slide forward on the seat to relieve the discomfort (Fig. 126). Recommended seat depth for 60% of the population would be 15" (381mm).

Fig.126. Radiograph of pressure behind knee due to seat being too deep. If depth of seat is too great, the front edge will press into area behind knee and the ensuing discomfort will make you move forward and off the backrest.

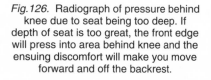

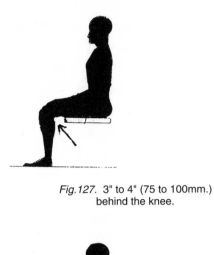

Fig.127. 3" to 4" (75 to 100mm.)
behind the knee.

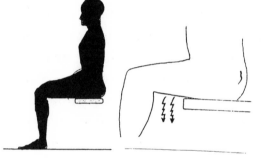

Fig.128. Inadequate thigh support
seat too short.

A good guideline is to ensure that the front edge is three finger widths or 3" to 4" (76mm to 103mm) behind the knee joint (Fig. 127). Seat depths of less than 13" (330mm) will not provide adequate support under the thighs (Fig. 128).

For lounge chairs, a depth of 18" to 20" (457mm to 508mm) is acceptable providing the seat height is approximately 14" (356mm), and the angle of the back rest is no greater than 28 to 30 degrees, or a head rest would be required for occasional support.

The depth of the seat should account for the fact that most people do not put their buttocks against the backrest, and its function as a supporting structure is therefore lost, encouraging slumping and poor posture. It is unfortunate that depth is not given more consideration in basic design criteria. In general terms, comfort and efficiency are more a function of dimensions than price tag. Providing the correct dimensions in a chair are not difficult, and until people become more discriminating and put comfort where it should be — at the top of the criteria list — chairs will continue to be designed with no relationship to anatomy, but rather to give the designer an opportunity to "make a statement", whatever that may mean!!!

5. The Backrest

For many chairs, the word backrest is a complete misnomer; although it should rest the back, this appears to be its least function. Rather it has evolved to give a chair balance, shape and individuality. Manufacturers know it is eye appeal that first attracts a buyer, not comfort. This is unfortunate because, although the back support allows so much scope for imaginative design, and has therefore received most of the interest and experiment in chair development, it is commonplace to see the research ignored. To be fair, there are many chairs today with excellent backrests, but there are also an extraordinary large number of chairs whose designs ignore the fundamental principles of shape (anatomy), and dimension (anthropometry).

There is clear evidence that the human body was no more designed for sitting than the feet for wearing shoes, and like shoes which you try on before purchase, with chairs, this means you should request a 24 hour trial period.

For comfortable sitting, blood circulation must not be impeded, and therefore no areas should be subjected to prolonged pressure. However, the points of contact with a chair are thighs, buttocks and back, and it is impossible not to subject these areas to some pressure. This being so, frequent changes of position become necessary and inevitable. Extensive videotaping of seated operators indicates that people change position on a chair at least once every five to eight minutes. A suitably designed backrest has the potential for increasing this interval, and it is this function that gives it priority in design next to seat height.

It is interesting and contrary to expectations, that internal pressure within the discs is actually higher in the sitting position than in standing, which is another reason why some people prefer to stand. Pressure on the discs in standing, due to gravity and the weight of the trunk, is to some degree modified or reduced by the support provided by the "guy ropes" concept of the back muscles and abdominal muscles holding the trunk erect. In sitting, abdominal muscles are relaxed, support in front is lost and pressure in the lumbar discs consequently rises.

Also not widely appreciated, is that when sitting, the pelvis is rotated backwards to bring the ischial tuberosities under the buttocks, flattening the lumbar curve (Fig. 129). This can only be achieved by some flexion of the lumbar vertebrae, accompanied by compression of the anterior borders of the discs forcing the nucleus (sac) inside to be compressed and

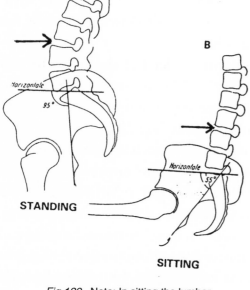

Fig.129. Note; In sitting the lumbar vertebrae are compressed anteriorly which must increase posterior disc pressure.

squeezed posteriorly (backwards). If there is already some damage to the annulus by way of micro-traumatic degeneration, there is likely to be a considerable increase of intra-discal pressure on ligament, or nerve roots. Not only will this result in increased pain, but also the risk of a posterior herniation of the disc. This is why so many people with back problems cannot find a comfortable chair, and it is also why the lumbar support to maintain the lumbar curve is so important.

My recommendations for the backrest are as follows:-

(a)   Backrest Angle. The subjective angle of comfort for the back support varies, not only from individual to individual, but also for the purpose for which the chair was intended. For instance, a dining chair is more upright than a study chair, but a 110 degree angle as measured from the horizontal is a good general purpose angle for an alert yet comfortable position.

(b)   Lumbar Support. Since individual variations in height are so slight in this region, and the length of the lumbar spine in the tallest male is approximately $6\frac{1}{2}$" (165mm) to 8" (200mm), a lumbar support of the latter width will suit almost everyone (Fig. 130).

(c)   Studies indicate that the level of the lowest lumbar vertebra is approximately 7" (175mm) above the level of the seat, but allowing for a seat depression of 1" (25mm), the lower edge of the lumbar support should be approximately 6" (150mm) above the compressed seat. It is undesirable for the backrest to extend below this point and into the sacral region, because the buttocks tend to "spread" in sitting, and a solid backrest here will force the sitter to slide forward on the seat. The lower edge of the backrest must, therefore, be above and clear of the sacral region, so that one can comfortably oppose the lumbar spine to the backrest (Fig. 130). If the backrest extends down to meet the seat cushion, the buttock zone must be very softly padded and offer no resistance.

(d)   The proper use of the back rest is only possible if you can sit back far enough to reach it, without a sense of

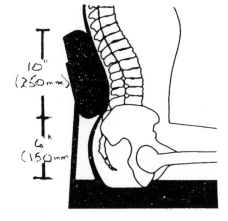

Fig. 130. Good seating, supporting the lumbar spine - 6" between the compressed seat and the lower edge of lumbar support and 10" backrest width.

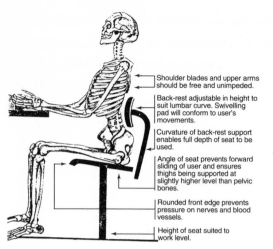

Shoulder blades and upper arms should be free and unimpeded.

Back-rest adjustable in height to suit lumbar curve. Swivelling pad will conform to user's movements.

Curvature of back-rest support enables full depth of seat to be used.

Angle of seat prevents forward sliding of user and ensures thighs being supported at slightly higher level than pelvic bones.

Rounded front edge prevents pressure on nerves and blood vessels.

Height of seat suited to work level.

Fig. 131. Good backrest and seat relationship.

Fig. 132. A "hitching rail" type seat for a powerepress operator who had to have free trunk movement. The seat originally cost $120 N.Z. and was virtually indestructable.

discomfort in the lower legs (Fig. 131). Thus, it is very dependent on the correlation to seat depth. It should then be firm enough to give adequate support to that part of the trunk resting on it. This does not mean that it must necessarily be fixed. Spring loaded supports are excellent, provided the spring is strong enough to resist the full weight of the trunk, or it creates a feeling of insecurity. It should also be noiseless and the ability to adjust the tension in the springs should not be beyond the strength of the weakest female. You should not require the services of "Mr Universe" to adjust your chair.

(e)   A backrest should also not restrict the movements of the arms, thus total support of the whole back for a work or dining chair is not recommended. A criteria to control this is that the height of the upper edge of the backrest must be clear of the lower (inferior) angle of the shoulder blade (scapula) or arm movement is impeded (See Fig. 131 again). This fixes the overall height for a work or dining chair at approximately 16" (406mm) from compressed seat level. However, an armchair whose function is pure relaxation can be appreciably higher.

Concluding this important chapter, there is no sound reason to tolerate 20 or 30 different chairs in a plant, particularly as designs change so frequently. The maintenance of chairs is always a low priority and an inability to get replacement parts increases this reluctance. A visit to the "salvage" department of any plant or institution will confirm this.

Designing chairs is not difficult and you can do it quite successfully yourself. Just make sure you are aware of the function you expect from the chair and respect the dimensions of the group who will be sitting on it (Fig. 132).

Three chair designs could suffice for your plant; a process worker's chair, an administrative office chair, and an executive chair. If you do not wish to design them yourself, then gather up all the brochures, decide what best suits your operation, obtain samples for operators' approval, make your selection and let these become your standard chairs. Ensure there is an after sales service. Never buy a chair that suits your eye, but rather the part of the anatomy that will sit on it. As I have said, this is not necessarily a function of price, but of simply being more discriminating and more caring, because your decision will ultimately make the difference between comfort or a pain in the butt. . . . !

Chapter 15
PREVENTING BACK INJURIES AT HOME

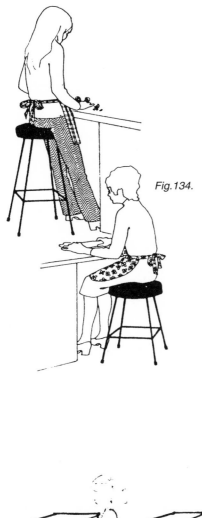

Fig. 134.

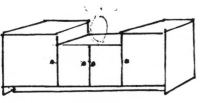

Fig. 135.

1. KITCHEN

Traditionally, most of the work done in a kitchen is performed standing at a bench. This is fatiguing and unnecessary; some of the food preparation and certainly the washing of dishes could be carried out more comfortably with a hitching rail type seat or a high stool to take the weight off the feet (Fig. 134). A space under the sink area will accommodate this function very nicely and it can be effectively covered by doors when not required.

The amount of standing makes bench height a critical dimension and I recommend 37" (940mm), which is higher than the 35$\frac{1}{2}$" (900mm) standard bench height and encourages better posture. A recess in the kitchen bench top of approximately 6" (150mm) (Fig. 135), will allow activities demanding heavy downward pressure from the shoulders, as in kneading dough to be done with less strain whilst maintaining a better overall height relationship.

2. CUPBOARDS

Look critically at the design of storage in your kitchen and how you use it. Ideally, the items most in use should be located on the shelves from which no stooping or stretching is required, that, is between waist and shoulder level. Cupboards above or below this height should be reserved for long

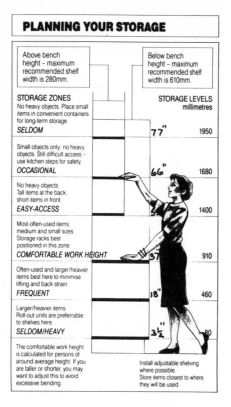

PLANNING YOUR STORAGE

Above bench height – maximum recommended shelf width is 280mm.		Below bench height – maximum recommended shelf width is 610mm.

STORAGE ZONES

STORAGE LEVELS millimetres

No heavy objects. Place small items in convenient containers for long-term storage.
SELDOM — 77" — 1950

Small objects only: no heavy objects. Still difficult access – use kitchen steps for safety.
OCCASIONAL — 66" — 1680

No heavy objects. Tall items at the back, short items in front.
EASY-ACCESS — 1400

Most-often-used items: medium and small sizes. Storage racks best positioned in this zone.
COMFORTABLE WORK HEIGHT — 37" — 910

Often-used and larger/heavier items best here to minimise lifting and back strain.
FREQUENT — 18" — 460

Larger/heavier items. Roll-out units are preferable to shelves here.
SELDOM/HEAVY — 3½" — 80

The comfortable work height is calculated for persons of around average height. If you are taller or shorter, you may want to adjust this to avoid excessive bending.

Install adjustable shelving where possible. Store items closest to where they will be used.

Fig. 136. (From ACC. N.Z.)

Fig. 137. A bolt at floor level is not a good idea. A bolt 20" (500mm.) from the floor is a good idea.

term storage, such as preserves or infrequently used pots and pans. Do not store electrical appliances on high shelves. Crockery or vegetable racks in constant use should be at a comfortable height, not at floor level (Fig. 136). Maximum vertical reach height for a cupboard is 1780mm (70"). If it is over a counter, the height should be reduced to 1680mm (66") (Fig. 136).

Pots and pans in constant use are better placed hanging on the wall where access is much easier.

Appliances used every day should have a permanent place on the counter top near a power outlet, or on an easily accessible shelf.

A few minutes study of your kitchen to determine your lifting priorities could mean a dramatic change to an aching back. (Fig. 137).

3. STOVES AND OVENS

The appliances fitted into a kitchen justify just as much consideration as the bench height. Unfortunately, manufacturers have designed their equipment to fit the standard bench height, which in turn requires kitchen designers to perpetuate the $35^1/_2$" (900mm) standard, so that the stove top lines up with the bench. Should you ever redesign your kitchen, the optimum is an overall height of 37" to $38^1/_2$" (940mm to 978mm), which is 2" to 3" (50mm to 75mm) below the elbow height of the average adult. (Humanscale 7).

Some oven designs force a person to bend at a hazardous angle to open the door. As you get older, your muscles are getting weaker, the family is growing up and the dishes are getting bigger (Fig. 138). If you have an oven of this type, first leave the dish on the kitchen bench until with bent knees you

Fig.138. Never put dishes in an oven like this. Your back is not a crane.

Fig.139. This is much more sensible.

Fig.140.

open the oven door, straighten up, take the roast, and this time, bending your knees again place it in the oven (Fig. 139). Taking it out is the reverse procedure.

If you can afford it or intend to remodel your kitchen, get an eye level oven. I believe it is a necessity in any kitchen. With this type of oven, the door should cantilever upwards in a frontal plane. Downward opening doors mean you are always some distance from the oven and will have to adopt a straight knee, flexed back posture to place anything inside. With side opening doors, ensure the door is hinged to open on your work area side. (In most side opening doors, the door can be modified to open from either side). You may have to search for an oven of this type, but they are available and with some makes, can be specified. Its well worth the effort.

4. THE BED

Making beds can be hazardous for backs (Fig. 140). If I was asked to rate the order of the causes of home back injuries, I would place beds immediately below stoves. The only thing that stops them from being rated higher is the duration of risk. Beds are generally made once a day, but according to the U.S. Department of Agriculture, the average houseperson walks 4 miles (6.5km) and spends 25 hours each year making beds.

High rents and rising property values are making houses and apartments smaller; invariably, bedrooms have a low priority in accommodation layout.

Beds tend to be placed in corners to give the bedroom an illusion of space. This is dangerous, because of the reluctance to move the bed in order to make it, thus reaching the other side of a single bed is generally attempted by keeping the knees straight and flexing the trunk to such an acute angle

121

Fig. 141. This is hazardous for any back.

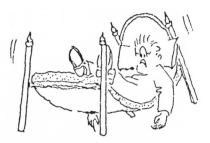

Fig. 142. Exposed wire coil bases eventually look like this.

Solid timber base

Fig. 143. This is better!

that even balancing on two feet becomes difficult. This is asking for trouble, particularly as you get older. Wider than normal beds, such as a "Queen" size, increases the hazard.

Beds should be placed, either in the centre of a room, or if they have to be in a corner, mounted on good castors so they can be pulled out easily to let you get to both sides for tucking in blankets and sheets. The only option to this is to consider using a continental quilt or duvet, which minimises the procedure.

Whatever the conditions applying to your bedroom, beds still have to be physically made up. This should be done by bending on one or both knees and not as in illustration 141.

Beds should be firm but not hard. A 6" to 8" (150mm to 200mm minimum) foam rubber or innersprung mattress is satisfactory. This applies equally to waterbeds, which must be of the compartment type construction to be fairly firm.

With the depth of the cervical and lumbar curves no greater than 75mm (3 inches) in the normal adult, the average quality mattress is quite sufficient to absorb the curves of the spine and provide adequate relaxation. Avoid bases made of exposed wire coils, they eventually lose their tension and tend to sag (Fig. 142). The end result is more like a hammock, with the mattress conforming to the shape of the base.

If you intend purchasing a new bed, consider a mattress and frame only. A mattress is structurally better resting on a base made of 12mm ($^1/_2$ inch), ply or coreboard, or even an old door. The Japanese have been sleeping on this type of bed for centuries. So when buying a new bed, avoid if you can purchasing the base. You are virtually wasting your money! (Fig. 143).

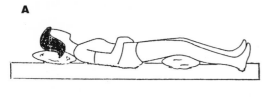

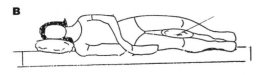

Fig.144 Recommended lying
positions.

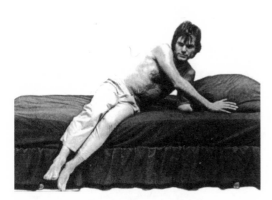

Fig.145. Recommended method of
getting out of bed, particularly in
the morning.

Again, as with chairs, the texture of a mattress is very personal. What is comfortable for one person, may be quite uncomfortable for another. Therefore, having a mattress on approval for a night or two is a good idea if you can get away with it. If this is not possible, try lying on it in the store for a reasonable period, and assess your responses before finally committing yourself to the purchase.

Recommend lying positions are shown in Figs. 144a, b). When getting out of bed in the morning, it is advisable to turn on your side and lever yourself up using your arms rather than sitting up from a back lying position. (Fig. 145).

A final comment on waterbeds. Many people prefer to sit on the edge of a bed to put on their socks and shoes. Waterbeds, surrounded by a box made of 25mm (1 inch) timber means that sitting over the edge for any reason can be quite uncomfortable. Remember, the chances are you will be growing older with this bed, and may never buy another. Whilst you may be able to accommodate a certain amount of discomfort now in the interests of fashion or trends, your tolerance will diminish with time and experience, and you may regret not giving it more consideration. Be advised!

5. LAUNDRY

Washing machines and dryers are normally the standard height, and whilst this is satisfactory for most top loading washers, the front loading dryer is a back hazard because some washing usually falls on the floor either during loading or unloading. Dryers are better placed on the wall, preferably above the washing machine, so that washing can be put directly into the dryer and taken out above a bench top.

Hanging washing out to dry in the sun and wind is still widely practised in many countries. This normally involves the backbreaking chore of carrying a heavy basket of washing a considerable distance to the clothes line, putting it down and picking it all up again one item at a time to hang them on the line. It is a fatiguing practice and can be modified by the use of a trundler on wheels, holding a suspended washable linen or plastic container. Where steps are involved, position the trundler permanently beyond the steps; the linen or plastic container is generally removable.

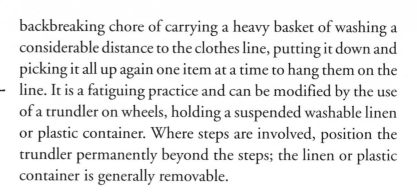

Bad Posture   Good Posture

Alternatively place a small weatherproof platform adjacent to the clothes line at a height of approximately 750mm (30"), and attach a box to the vertical supporting post for the clothes pegs.

6. GARDENING

The most dangerous activity for the production of back injuries in the average home is certainly gardening. People are so highly motivated in their gardens, they violate every rule of safety. They weed for hours, dig over enormous mounds of earth, reach up beyond their limit to prune plants or trees, carry sacks of fertiliser long distances, heave heavy pot plants, or are forever mowing lawns. Gardening should be approached from the point of view that the human spine is not a substitute for a wheelbarrow or a ladder. Use a long handled tool for cutting just out of reach shrubs or trees, and a long handled shovel for digging is much easier on your back. When planting or weeding, use a rubber kneeling pad, preferably with handles to assist going down or getting up from the ground. (Fig. 146).

Fig. 146. The correct way to weed.

A wheelbarrow is the equipment for moving heavy loads, such as sacks of fertiliser, earth or rocks. If the weight to be moved is a sack, first go down on one knee, as close to the sack as possible, lift with your arms and place it across your bent knee. Then straighten by extending the rear leg and tip the

Fig.147a,b. Use a wheelbarrow for
moving heavy loads.
Place the weight across your knee
and lift by extending the rear leg.

Fig.148. Hammocks don't even
look comfortable.

sack into the barrow. You will find this much easier and worth the extra time. (Fig. 147a, b)

Make sure you have a step or trestle ladder with safety feet for very tall plants, and reach within your limitations. Do not carry heavy or awkward loads up or down ladders, whatever the urgency or the temptation. Get Help! Be sensible about gardening; make it a pleasure by not giving yourself impossible targets. In the long run, a few less flowers or vegetables will make very little difference.

If you like reading in the garden, don't use a hammock. It looks decorative and inviting, but you will need to be gymnast to get in and out of it, and its not good for backs. (Fig. 148).

7. TRASH CANS

The lifting and carrying of loaded trash bags or garden refuse should be undertaken with more respect for the spine. Ensure that distance walked with the garbage to its collecting point outside the house is the absolute minimum, the path in good order and free of obstructions. Many local councils are now issuing plastic bins on wheels, which is an excellent method of holding rubbish and should be more universally available. In any event, if your system is via a paper sack, bend your knees to lift it.

8. SWEEPING AND VACUUMING

Take care in sweeping or vacuuming; the forced flexion of the spine for long periods is not good postural positioning and you may find it difficult to straighten up for some hours. Extend the length of the broom by fitting a longer handle, even 150mm (6") makes a significant difference, and the cost

Fig.149. Vacuming a house is a long, posturally arduous task. A 6" (150mm.) extension for the handle is advisable.

is negligible. With vacuum cleaners, invest in an extra segment to extend the hose (Fig. 149). When sweeping or vacuuming, try to keep your back fairly straight; and to get under furniture, bend on one knee (Fig. 150a,bc,d.).

(a) Wrong   (b) Right   (c) Wrong   (d) Right

Fig.150. Use a long handled broom for sweeping. 6" longer makes a significant difference.

When sweeping under cupboards go down on one knee.

9. STAIRS

Unsafe stairs produce falls. It is a common factor of falls that, at the moment you think you are going to fall, you instinctively jerk backwards and add a back injury to anything else you might suffer. Unsafe stairs are those that are uneven, badly placed or vary in size where the risors or treads differ from the architectural standards of internal or external stairs, and where the danger is therefore not anticipated. For internal stairs, risors should be between 175 to 200mm (7" to 8") and treads between 230 to 280mm (9" to 11"). (Figs. 151a, b, c, d)

Fig.151a. A single step in an unexpected place is dangerous.

Fig.151b. Handrails should continue on the landing to mark the end of the stairs

Fig.151c. Winders are likely to cause falls.

Fig.151d. A projecting step is a hazard.

The last step is always the most hazardous, particularly when carrying something down, and should be well defined with a contrasting stripe on the nosing. The handrail should function as a guide by continuing for a short distance beyond the landing, and also to warn you that you are at the last step. Stairs must be well lit with a two way remote switch conveniently situated for day and night accessibility.

Be sure of your footing

10. HOUSEHOLD REPAIRS

Household repairs and furniture moving are seldom done activities that tempt you to gamble with your safety.

Plan for emergencies

If you intend to move furniture, be prepared with rollers cut from old broom handles. Wear gloves. Plan the route you intend to take and ensure its free from tripping hazards. Determine where the object will be set down. Consider the distance the load is going to be moved and make sure there is enough space to turn and handle it safely (Figs 152 a, b, c). Plan rest stops if necessary.

Always spend a little time planning ahead with repairs, so that you will not be caught holding something heavy in an awkward position. Have a light in your attic or basement with a remote switch in the garage or house.

Fig.152a, b, c. Organise and plan ahead your household repairs.

Cleaning windows should be done within easy reach limits, whether a ladder is used or not. Do not allow yourself to be tempted to overreach.

Chapter 16
First Aid After a Back Injury

1. THE SEVERE INJURY

Remember we are discussing non-pathological back conditions, and if you have just witnessed a traumatic back injury like somebody falling from a height, whether they are unconscious or not, DO NOT MOVE THEM. The best you can do is get a doctor and ambulance immediately and see that they are kept warm. It is always possible they have fractured a vertebrae. For this reason, even lifting their head to put a pillow under it could be dangerous; you might convert what is perhaps a simple compression fracture to a fracture/ dislocation with consequent complications that could include injury to the spinal cord and paralysis.

If it is necessary to move the patient to a safer place, use a solid stretcher, and have several people on either side to hold the patient steady. Keep the body straight.

2. THE MILD BACK INJURY

The characteristic discomfort from a back problem stems as much from the muscle spasm as the inflammatory response to the injury. This, as you have read in earlier chapters, is the body's response to musculo-skeletal injury, and is a muscle's self defence reaction to limit further damage. Movement is therefore inhibited.

However, muscle spasm and the resulting stiffness can be as

painful as the condition itself, and adds substantially to the discomfort. It is often the first symptom to arrive and the last to go.

Since the average traumatic back condition will subside in due course, almost regardless of the treatment administered, the relief of pain is the first consideration, and a good hot shower is the best first aid available to you. Let the water run on the painful area as hot and as hard as you can tolerate for at least 5 to 10 minutes. Muscles relax in the presence of heat, which is why a hot bath is so relaxing. The weight of the water raining down on you is good hydrotherapy and has effects similar to massage for relieving the muscle spasm.

Whilst under the shower, gently carry out the pelvic tilting exercise as discussed in Chapter 10 and a few knee bends, as described in Chapter 8. Exercise at this period is for mobility more than strength, and between 8 to 12 repetitions performed very gently would be sufficient.

Continue this regime until you feel comfortable enough to slowly start your full exercise program. Your muscles will be a little stiff and uncomfortable, but be cautious, persevere, take it easily, and you will be pleased with the result.

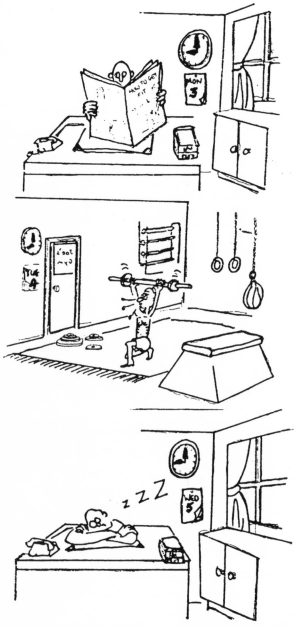

Fig. 153. Exercise Intelligently!

RESPECT PAIN

Pain is the body's danger signalling system, and should never be underestimated. It is an indication that the injury has not yet recovered. In terms of your back, if the pain is really uncomfortable, it is saying you are not yet ready for exercise or are going too far, either in range or repetition. Don't be a masochist and think if it hurts, it must be doing you good, this is simply not true and you could very easily start the whole cycle over again.

Exercise following a back injury should be carried out under your doctor's directions and within a relatively pain free threshold, moving only slightly into the pain range. Slowly, as the pain threshold decreases, you can increase the range and strength of your activities.

REST

Over the years, rest has evolved as an important element in the immediate treatment of a back injury; it has also become one of the most controversial. The purpose of rest is to allow any inflammatory reaction that is present to subside. The relief achieved may or may not be permanent. However, the subsequent muscle spasm and resulting stiffness is likely to continue for a varying period after the inflammatory reaction has subsided, and prolonged bed rest, which may debilitate the patient, is unnecessary and counter productive.

A randomised study of 203 patients with mechanical low pain treated with either two or seven days bed rest, found that those with two days of bed rest lost fewer days of work and had no difference in symptoms at follow up. (Deyo R.A. et al. N.Engl.J.Med.1986.315. 1064-1070).

In acute pain, where any movement is extremely painful, two or three days bed rest should be considered maximum with the patient up and making small walks as soon as possible to maintain mobility and muscle tone. Sitting, except for very short periods, should be avoided during this phase.

SWIMMING

Excellent, but read Chapter 11.

SEX

I repeat, either before or after a back injury, sex is excellent and should be practiced diligently!!

CONCLUSION

As you can see, back injuries are the result of many things; genetic inheritance, stature, fitness, what you lift, how you lift, its weight, its size, its shape and possibly a poor ergonomic work environment.

I firmly believe we can reduce this relentless toll of pain, suffering and disability if we accept the fact that we now have the knowledge to do so. But the pathway to control is paved with awareness. We need to open our minds, and stop accepting back pain with some kind of philosophic resignation, and in particular, understand that human beings like machines have limitations that must be respected.

Take a good, hard, practical look at your home and work environment, and decide whether the amount of bending and lifting you are doing is really necessary. Design out unnecessary bending. I have seen things picked up, simply to be moved to another location for no real reason other than "this is how it was always done!"

Condition yourself to lift with your legs. People wear out regardless of their life styles, but they hurry it along with bad bending habits and poor occupational postures.

Whether it is a houseperson in a kitchen or a worker at a factory bench, we have the knowledge today to control back injuries, and it is so easy to apply, it is almost sheer negligence to suffer a disabling back injury.

After all, we accept uncritically the necessity for personal hygiene, why not also include back care. Bend your knees is to the spine what brushing your teeth is to tooth decay. To become effective, it must be viewed as one of the disciplines of daily living.

Every back injury to me is a personal affront, and I would like to feel we all share a common obligation to do everything possible to prevent back injuries everywhere, as well as to ourselves. You now have information you did not have when you started your journey through this book. You have more knowledge on how the back wears out and why it wears out, and hopefully you know your limitations.

I also hope what has been said will be seen as an exercise in common sense, and if you agree with the basic premise, you will feel motivated to adopt it. In its simplest possible terms, I am appealing to you in the interests of your back to make three commitments from this moment on.

The first is that you BEND YOUR KNEES regardless of what you intend to pick up or put down. Set a personal example, if not for yourself then for others perhaps dependent on you, parents, wives, husbands, and particularly children, who learn by example.

The second is (if you do not have time to exercise) at least do the PELVIC TILTING and DEEP KNEE BENDS exercises described in the earlier chapters every day (including today), and hereafter.

The third is, to KEEP YOUR WEIGHT DOWN.

Finally, we occasionally have to be our brother's keeper, and if you see someone who is known to you lifting incorrectly, I am asking you to tell them; they may choose to ignore your advice, but equally they may accept it, and if you can be instrumental in preventing one back injury, this book will have been worthwhile.

Undoubtably, our life styles and longevity are making our spines more vulnerable. One of the primary aims of this project is to make the problem more understandable without the necessity to study a voluminous number of text books, so often a prerequisite before embarking on any anatomical and physiological work of this nature.

Having read my book, I hope it has achieved its objective and it is now more evident to you that the functional condition of your back as you get older is to a large degree in your hands. I would like to believe that I have convinced you sufficiently to change a few habit patterns whilst there is still time to prevent you from becoming another back statistic.

Remember, you only have one back and it is not a crane. Treat it with care and it will give you a lifetime of service and pleasure, or you can disregard this advice and take your chances on degeneration, disability and perhaps even surgery. The choice is yours! The answer is simple: USE YOUR KNEES WHENEVER YOU GO TOWARDS THE FLOOR, NOT YOUR BACK!

Leonard Ring
Auckland,
New Zealand 1993

BIBLIOGRAPHY

Anderson, J.A. "Back Pain and Occupation" The Lumbar Spine and Back Pain. 2nd.Ed. 1979.

Armstrong, J.R. "Lumbar Disc Lesions" 2nd Ed. 1958, Livingstone Ltd.

Australian Government Publishing Service, "Safe Manual Handling, Draft Code of Practice", Canberra, 1986.

Ayoub, M.M. et al. "Development of strength and capacity norms for manual materials handling activities. The state of the art". J. Human Factors. 1980. 22. 271-283. (b) 1980.

Ayoub, M.M. "Work Place Design and Posture" J.Human F. 15 (3) 1973.

Battie, M.C., Bigos, S.J. et al. "The Role of Spinal Flexibility in Back Pain Complaints within Industry" J.Spine, Vol.15, No.8, 1990.

Bartelink, D.L. "The Role of Abdominal Pressure on the Lumbar Intervertebral Disc" J.Bone, Jnt.Surg. 39B, 1957.

Belbin, E. "The Effects of Propaganda on Recall, Recognition and Behaviour" Brit.J.Psy. 47. 1956.

Bigos, S.J., Battie, M.C. et al. "A Prospective Study of Work Perceptions and Psychosocial Factors Affecting the Report of Back Injury". J.Spine Vol.16. No.1. 1991.

Bigos, S.J., Spengler, D.M. et al. "Back Injuries in Industry: A Retrospective Study" J.Spine, Vol.11, No.3. 1986.

Brown, J.R. "Manual Lifting and Related Fields" Labour Safety Council of Ontario, Ministry of Labour, 1972.

Brown, J.R. "Factors involved in the causation of weightlifting accidents". J. Ergonomics, 2 (1) 1958.

Brown, Todd, R. et al. "Ergonomics in the U.S. Railroad Industry" Human Factors Society Bulletin, March 1991, Vol. 34, No. 3.

Consumer Review, "Chiropractic, Fact and Fiction" No.9. Feb. 1976. Consumer Institute, Wellington, N.Z.

Cailliet, R. "Low Back Pain Syndrome" 2nd.Ed.1968, F.A. Davis, Co. Philadelphia.

Chapanis, A. "The Relevance of Laboratory Studies to Practical Situations, J.Ergonomics, Vol.10, No.5. 1967.

Congleton, J.J. et al. "An evaluation of a weightlighting belt and back injury prevention training class for airline baggage handlers". J.App. Erg. Oct.1992. Vol.23. No.5.

Davies, D.V. and Davies, F. "Gray's Anatomy" 33rd.Ed. 1962.

Dan, N.G. and Sacassan, P.A. "Serious Complications of Lumbar Spine Manipulations", J. of Aust.Med. 2, 1983.

Drury, C.G. and Francher, M. "Evaluation of a forward sloping chair" J.App.Erg.1985. 16.1.

Eagle, R. "Pain in the Back", New Scientist, 18/18/1979

Elnaggar, M.I. "Effects of Spinal Flexion and Extension Exercises on Low-Back Pain and Spinal Mobility in Chronic Mechanical Low-Back Pain Patients", J. Spine, Vol.16, No.8, 1991.

Frymoyer, J.W. "Epidemiological Survey, Risk Factors in Low Back

Pain", J. Bone Joint Surg. 65A, 1983.

Frost, Helen, "Physiotherapy Management of Low Pack Pain" J.Physio. U.K. Oct.1992. Vol.78. No.10.

Garg, Run. "What Criteria Exists for Determining How Much Load Can Be Lifted Safely" J. Human Factors, 1980, 22 (4).

Godfrey, C.M. et al. "A Randomised Trial For Manipulation For Low Back Pain", J. Spine, 9. 1984.

Grandjean, E. "Fitting the task to the man" London, Taylor and Francis Ltd,. 1969.

Hall, H.W. "The Hip Flex Theory of Lifting", U.S.A. 1968.

Harman, E. A. et. al. 1989 "Effects of a belt on intra-abdominal pressure during weightlifting" Medical Science in Sports and Exercise, 21(2) U.S.A.

Heineman, London, "Human Kinetics and Analysing Body Movement" Ch.17. 1951. J.A.M.A. "Conservative Therapy for Low Back Pain; Distinguishing Useful from Useless Therapy", 250, 1983.

Heathershaw, Richard. "Manual Handling, The Consultative Document" J. Protection, U.K. Oct. 1982.

International Labour Office, Meetings of experts on the maximum permissable weight to be carried by one worker. Geneva, M.P.W./ 1965/14, 1965.

Jayson, M.I.V. "The Lumbar Spine and Back Pain", 2nd. Ed. Pitman Med.Intra. 1979.

Jayson, M. "Backache a Matter of Structural Stress" New Scie. 8/12/76.

Kapandji, I.A. "The Physiology of the Joints", Churchill Livingstone Press, London and New York, Vol.3. 1979.

Kendall, H.O. and F.P. "Posture and Pain", Boynton, D.A. Williams and Williams, Balt.

Krolner, B. and Toft, B. "Vertebral Bone Loss: An unheeded side effect of therapeutic bed rest", Clin.Soc. U.S.A. 64. 1983.

Kelsey, J. L. and White, A.A. "Epidemiology and impact of low back pain", J. Spine, 5. 1980.

LaBan, M.M. et al. "Pregnancy and the Herniated Lumbar Disc", Arch.Phys.Med. Rehabil. 64. 1983.

Lageard, P. and Robinson, M. "Back Pain, Current Concepts and Recent Advances" Short Rpt. on 1st International Congress on Back Pain. Vienna, Nov. 1985. J.Physio. Vol.72. Feb. 1986.

Lankhorst, G.J. et al. "The Effect of the Swedish Back School in Chronic Ideopathic Low Back Pain", A prospective controlled study. Scand.J. Rehabil. Med.15. 1983.

Macnab, I. "Backache", 4th. Ed. 1981. Waverley Press Inc. Balt. MD. U.S.A.

McGill, S.M. et. al. "The effect of an abdominal belt on trunk muscle activity and intra-abdominal pressure during squat lifts" J. Ergonomics, 1990, Vol. 33, No. 2.

Mandal, A.C. "The Seated Man (Homo Sedens) The seated work

position theory and practice". J.App.Erg. 1981. 12.1

Nachemson, A. "A Critical Look at Conservative Treatment for Low Back Pain", The Lumbar Spine and Back Pain, 2nd. Ed. 1980. Pitman Med. Books.

Nachemsom, A. "The Effect of Forward Leaning on Lumbar Intradiscal Pressure", Acta. Orthop. Scand. Supp. 43.1 1960.

National Safety Council, "Accident Facts", 1985–1990. Chicago.

NIOSH Tech.Rpt. "Work Practices Guide for Manual Lifting", Pub. No. 81–122 U.S. Dept. of Health and Human Services.

NIOSH Tech.Rpt. "Safety in Manual Materials Handling", Pub. 78–185 U.S. Dept of Health, Education and Welfare.

NMHC. Conference, 1982. "Manual Handling," Logistics Today", National Materials Handling Centre, U.K.

Orthopaedic Knowledge Update No.2. "Lumbar Spine" Ch.28. P.311. American Academy of Orth.Surg.

Poulson, E. and Jorgenson, A. "Back Muscle Strength and Stooped Work Postures", J.App.Erg. 1971.

Protection, Journal "Manual Handling, The Consultative Document", U.K. Oct. 1982.

Rickenbacher J. and Landholt, A.M. et al. "Applied Anatomy of the Back", Springer-Verlag, Berlin.

Ring, L. "Back Injuries and Safety Propaganda in Manual Handling", Unpublished M.Sc. Thesis Loughborough Univ. of Tech. U.K. 1974.

Ring, L. "The Role of Physiotherapy in the Prevention of Industrial Accidents", N.Z.Jn of Physio. 3. (13)

Ring, L. "Awareness V. Performance in Back Injury Prevention", J.Prof.Saf. U.S.A. July, 1989.

Robertson, L.S. and Keeve, J.P. "Worker Injuries. The Effects of Workers' Compensation and OSHA Inspections", J. Health Polit. Policy Law 8. 1983.

Rodgers, S.H. "Working with Backache", Perinton Press, N.Y. 1985.

Roland, M. and Morris, R. "A Study of the Natural History of Back Pain", Part 1. Development of a Reliable and Sensitive Measure of Disability in Low-Back Pain. J.Spine, Vol.8. No.2. 1983.

Rosen, N.B. "Treating the many facets of pain". Business and Health; 7–10 May, 1986.

Rowe, M.L. "Backache at Work", Perinton Press, N.Y.

Snook, S.H. "The Design of Manual Handling Tasks", J.Prof.Saf. U.S.A. May 1980.

Snook, S.H. "Low Back Pain", Liberty Mutual Insurance Co. U.S.A.

Snook, S.H. "Approaches to the Control of Back Pain in Industry: Job Design, Job Placement and Education Training", J.Spine. Vol.2. No.1. Sept. 1988.

Snook, S.H; Irvine, C.H. and Bass, S.F. "Maximum weights and Work Loads Acceptable to Male Industrial Workers" Am. Ind. Hyg. Assoc. J. 31. 1970.

Snook, S.H. and Ciriello, V.M. "Maximum weights and Work Loads Acceptable to Female Workers" J. Occup. Med. 16:527-534. 1974b.

Tichauer, E.R. "Biomechanics of Lifting, A Pilot Study", P.69. Instit. of Rehab.Med. N.Y.Univ.Med. Centre.

The Safety Practitioner Journal, "Reducing Lifting and Handling Accidents", U.K. Dec. 1985.

Time Magazine, "That Aching Back", July 14th. 1980.

Tomecek. Sharon, "Shop Smart to Help your Workers Backs" J. Safety and Health, National Safety Council, U.S.A. Nov. 1992.

Troup, J.D.G. "Industry and the Low Back Problem", The New Scientist, Jan. 1970.

Ward, Joan, A critique of the "Mandal" chair. J.Design, U.K. 333